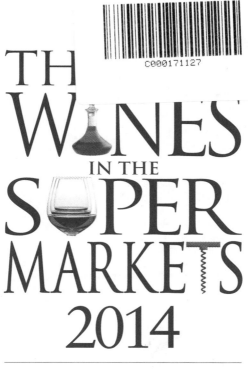

THE WINES IN THE SUPERMARKETS 2014

NED HALLEY

foulsham
LONDON • NEW YORK • TORONTO • SYDNEY

C000171127

foulsham

Capital Point, 33 Bath Road, Slough, Berkshire
SL1 3UF, England

Foulsham books can be found in all good bookshops and direct from
www.foulsham.com

ISBN: 978-0-572-04417-6

Text copyright © 2013 Ned Halley
Series, format and layout design © W. Foulsham & Co. Ltd

Cover photographs © Thinkstock

A CIP record for this book is available from the British Library

The moral right of the author has been asserted

Typeset in the UK by Chris Brewer Origination
Printed and bound in Great Britain by Martins the Printers Ltd

Contents

We've never had it so good

There is so much good wine in the supermarkets it makes me want to weep. For joy, of course. But also for the thousands of dedicated grape-growers and winemakers across the world who create these wonderful products and have to sell them at knockdown prices to the rapacious retailers who now utterly dominate the business in Britain. And Britain, believe it or not, is the most important export market for wine worldwide.

As consumers of wine, we've never had it so good. But the wine producers have never had it so tough. Everybody wants to make wine, and supply has simply outgrown demand. The global recession hasn't helped. There has been a slump in sales in the wine-producing countries – France's thirst has halved in a generation – and the hoped-for exponential rise in consumption in major importing countries, including Britain, has been stifled by the effects of continued economic gloom. But at least we're still drinking wine here, in spite of the chronic austerity, ever-rising taxes and the 'alcohol-awareness' lobby.

And look on the bright side. The supermarkets are contributing, in their way, to the trend towards moderation. They are not demons, egging us on to binge-drinking; these companies are owned, managed and staffed by people every bit as sensible and well-meaning as everybody else. And if they have a common mission as far as wine is concerned, I believe it is to encourage customers to drink sensibly, and drink better. It makes sound enough commercial sense: persuade customers to buy more interesting and varied wines at higher prices, with corresponding uplifts in margin. The space taken up on the shelf by a £4 wine that will earn the retailer a few pence is precisely equal to that occupied by a £20 bottle that will earn the store a fiver.

All the retailers are certainly in the business of easing up the quality levels. While the cheaper bottles are (with exceptions) of perfectly respectable standards, there is a noticeable trend towards more individualistic wines. Even frills-free Lidl, making its début in these pages this year, has raised its game significantly, with an entirely new 'Wine Cellar' range that extends from interesting rarities such as Gros Plant from the Pays Nantais to a wholly unexpected St Emilion grand cru classé, Château Laroze 2007, at twenty quid – a price that turns out to be entirely warranted. Bottles, according to Lidl, were 'flying off the shelves' as soon as they arrived in the stores.

I have not enquired from the good people at Tesco whether their own classed-growth offering has been meeting with a similar response. Tesco invested heavily in the 2009 clarets (the vintage of the millennium, I am reliably informed), and is now selling them online through its terrifically dynamic and efficient website. Château Lafite is offered in six-bottle original wooden cases at a cool £4,800, including delivery. That's £800 a bottle, a monstrous price. But it's a bit of a bargain compared to what you'd pay at regal London merchant Berry Bros & Rudd, a more accustomed purveyor of this sort of wine. Berry's price, when I last looked, was

£5,000 in bond, which means that once the duty and VAT are added on, each bottle is costing you a shade above £1,000.

Maybe this is the shape of things to come. The supermarkets long ago captured the plonk market, largely extinguishing the high street merchants, and now they're setting about the 'fine wine' sector too. I suppose it's all part of the democratisation of wine-drinking, and as such must be a Good Thing.

For the moment, supermarket wine offerings still dwell largely in the entry-level and mid-price sectors. This certainly circumscribes the 550-odd wines that feature in this 2014 edition of *The Best Wines in the Supermarkets*. Prices continue to start at below £5. Yes, there are still decent wines to be had below a fiver, even though the 2013 Budget finally edged the excise duty per 75cl bottle of still wine past £2, which puts the tax take on a £4.99 bottle at £2.84, a lot more than half the value. A really decent wine at or under a fiver is a little miracle, and yet this year I have found nearly a dozen of them, just at Asda, and a good few more elsewhere.

It's a lot easier, of course, to pick out wines in the mid-price zone up to a tenner or so, and the great majority described in this edition falls squarely into that area. But don't let me go on too much about prices. We all know our own budgets, and must stick to them. The wines I have recommended at above £10, and the few, perish the idea, above £20, are included strictly on the basis that there might be a special occasion to shop for, or an urge to splurge that is unaccountably irresistible.

Let me add, finally on this topic, that many of the prices I have entered for the wines are, at best, approximations. I have taken them in good faith as given to me, but the retailers retain the right to alter them – frequently with what appears to be a quixotic whimsicality. It has a lot to do with perpetual promotions, of course. We all know by now that multibuy discounts and the like are mostly illusory – the supermarket ups the price by a hefty amount for a few weeks in anticipation, then cuts it back to create the illusion. Over time, I have become reasonably adept at spotting prices inflated for these evil purposes, and as a rule I leave the offending wines (usually mega-brands) out. But quite often the discounts are applied to wines whose standard shelf price is perfectly honest. So you might well find one of my recommendations cheaper than listed. This is especially true of the blanket offers the supermarkets now regularly make, reducing the prices across their entire ranges by, typically, 25 per cent, usually on purchases of six bottles or more, any mix, in the store. Sainsbury and Tesco do this several times a year, and both Marks & Spencer and Waitrose do it online. Majestic does it more or less permanently (a cautious 20 per cent rather than the carefree 25 of its giant competitors).

This sort of thing obviously skews my scoring system, which is based on value judgement. But never mind. I work on a scale of 0 to 10, and wines I like, I mark according to their price. If Waitrose's wondrous Cuvée Chasseur 2012 cost £9.99 instead of £4.99, it would not score the 10 I've given it in this edition. The low price is definitely part of this crackingly good Mediterranean red's considerable appeal. Meanwhile Georges Duboeuf Chiroubles 2011, which does cost £9.99 at Waitrose, is a Beaujolais so marvellous I have scored it 10. Maybe a logician or some such arbiter of sense would infer from this that I believe the Chiroubles is almost exactly twice as good as the Chasseur. Of course I intend no such relativism. It's not the message I intend to convey. But I couldn't possibly enter into an argument about it. And what if Waitrose were to discount the Chiroubles to, say, £7.99? They're quite capable of it. How would I score it then? 12 out of 10?

So please take my scoring system in the spirit intended – a very personal indication of how much I like the wine, with the price borne in mind. I write down the scores when tasting the wine, and all those at 6 or more go into the longlist from which the final selection is drawn. In the end, just a very few 6- or 7-scoring wines make the cut. They tend to be wines I fear might be overpriced, or that have somehow fallen short of their potential. The most widely allocated score is 8. These are really commendable wines at what I believe to be reasonable prices. A score of 9 signals special merit and value, and the maximum score goes to wines I believe deserve nothing less.

Besides the arcane matter of points allocation, let me also add a word about the alcohol levels and vintages given for the wines. I mention the alcohol-by-volume percentage given for those wines in which the level is either below 12 per cent, or 14 per cent upwards. For drinkers concerned to know if their wine is more or less than averagely alcoholic, I hope this is of some help.

Almost all the wines in the listings are made entirely or substantially from the harvest of the year stated on the label. If no date appears, the wine will be a blend from the harvests of two or more years. This is routine for some cheaper wines, and need not signify, except with dry whites which, on principle, are the better for being young and fresh. An undated dry white is best consumed at the first opportunity, if at all.

A sense of place

This book categorises the wines by nation of origin. It is largely to follow the manner in which retailers arrange their wines, but also because it is the country or region of origin that still most distinguishes one style of wine from another. True, wines are now commonly labelled most prominently with their constituent grape variety, but to classify all the world's wines into the small number of principal grape varieties would make for categories of an unwieldy size.

Chardonnay, Sauvignon Blanc and Pinot Grigio are overwhelmingly dominant among whites, and four grapes – Cabernet Sauvignon, Grenache, Merlot and Syrah (also called Shiraz) – account for a high proportion of red wines made worldwide.

But each area of production still – in spite of creeping globalisation – puts its own mark on its wines. Chardonnays from France remain (for the moment at least) quite distinct from those of Australia. Cabernet Sauvignon grown in a cool climate such as that of Bordeaux is a very different wine from Cabernet cultivated in the cauldron of the Barossa.

Of course there are 'styles' that winemakers worldwide seek to follow. Yellow, oaky Chardonnays of the type pioneered in South Australia are now made in South Africa, too – and in new, high-tech wineries in New Zealand and Chile, Spain and Italy. But the variety is still wide. Even though the 'upfront' high-alcohol wines of the New World have grabbed so much of the market, France continues to make the elegant wines it has always made in its classic regions. Germany still produces racy, delicate Rieslings, and the distinctive zones of Italy, Portugal and Spain make ever more characterful wines from indigenous grapes, as opposed to imported global varieties.

Among less expensive wines, the theme is, admittedly, very much a varietal one. The main selling point for most 'everyday' wines is the grape of origin rather than the country of origin. It makes sense, because the characteristics of various grape varieties do a great deal to identify taste. A bottle of white wine labelled 'Chardonnay' can reasonably be counted on to deliver that distinctive peachy or pineappley smell and soft, unctuous apple flavours. A Sauvignon Blanc should evoke gooseberries, green fruit and grassy freshness. And so on.

For all the domination of Chardonnay and Cabernet, there are plenty of other grape varieties making their presence felt. Argentina, for example, has revived the fortunes of several French and Italian varieties that had become near-extinct at home. And the grape that (in my view) can make the most exciting of white wines, the Riesling, is now doing great things in the southern hemisphere as well as at home in Germany.

Among the current market trends, the rise of rosé continues apace. Now accounting for one out of every eight bottles of still wine sold, the choice of pink brands has simply exploded. I have certainly found a greater number of interesting pinks than might have been imagined a few years ago, but there are still plenty of dull ones with suspiciously high levels of residual sugar, so choose carefully.

Rosé wines are supposed to be made from black-skinned grapes. After the crush, the skins are left in contact with the juice for long enough to impart a pleasing colour, and maybe some flavour with it, and the liquids and solids are then separated before the winemaking process continues as it would for white wine.

Some rosés are made merely by blending red and white wines together. Oddly enough, this is how all (bar one or two) pink champagnes are made, as permitted under the local appellation rules. But under prevailing regulations in Europe, the practice is otherwise forbidden. Elsewhere in the world, where winemaking is very much less strictly standardised, blending is no doubt common enough.

It is, I know, a perpetual source of anguish to winemakers in tightly regulated European nations that they have to compete in important markets like Britain with producers in Australia, the Americas and South Africa who can make and label their wines just as they please. Vineyard irrigation, the use of oak chips, and the blending in of wines from other continents are all permitted in the New World and eschewed in the Old.

But would we have it any other way? No winemaker I have met in Bordeaux or Barolo, Bernkastel or Rias Baixas seriously wants to abandon the methods and conventions that make their products unique – even with an eye on creating a global brand. And in this present difficult economic climate for wine drinkers (and winemakers) worldwide, this assurance of enduring diversity is a comfort indeed.

Spot the grape variety

The character of most wines is defined largely by the grape variety, and it is a source of innocent pleasure to be able to identify which variety it is without peeking at the label. Here are some of the characteristics to look for in wines from the most widely planted varieties.

White

Chardonnay: Colour from pale to straw gold. Aroma can evoke peach, pineapple, sweet apple. Flavours of sweet apple, with creaminess or toffee from oak contact.

Fiano: Italian variety said to have been cultivated from ancient Roman times in the Campania region of southern Italy. Now widely planted on the mainland and in Sicily, it makes dry but soft wines of colours ranging from pale to pure gold with aromas of honey, orchard fruit, almonds and candied apricot. Well-made examples have beautifully balanced nutty-fresh flavours. Fiano is becoming fashionable.

Pinot Grigio: In its home territory of north-east Italy, it makes wines of pale colour, and pale flavour too. What makes the wine so popular might well be its natural low acidity. Better wines are more aromatic, even smoky, and pleasingly weighty in the manner of the Pinot Gris made in Alsace – now being convincingly imitated in both Argentina and New Zealand.

Riesling: In German wines, pale colour, sharp-apple aroma, racy fruit whether dry or sweet. Faint spritz common in young wines. Petrolly hint in older wines. Australian and New Zealand Rieslings have more colour and weight, and often a minerally, limey twang.

Sauvignon Blanc: In the dry wines, pale colour with suggestions of green. Aromas of asparagus, gooseberries, nettles, seagrass. Green, grassy fruit.

Semillon: Colour can be rich yellow. Aromas of tropical fruit including pineapple and banana. Even in dry wines, hints of honey amid fresh, fruit-salad flavours.

Viognier: Intense pale-gold colour. Aroma evokes apricots, blanched almonds and fruit blossom. Flavours include candied fruits. Finish often low in acidity.

Red

Cabernet Sauvignon: Dense colour, purple in youth. Strong aroma of blackcurrants and cedar wood ('cigar box'). Flavour concentrated, often edged with tannin so it grips the mouth.

Gamay: One of the most distinctive grapes of France, where it is the exclusive variety in the red wines of Beaujolais. Colour can be purple, with a suggestion of blue; nose evokes new-squashed raspberries, and there may be a hint of pear drops, an effect of carbonic maceration, a vinification technique used in Beaujolais. Fruit flavours are notably summery, juicy and refreshing.

Grenache: Best known in the Côtes du Rhône, it tends to make red wines pale in colour but forceful in flavour with a wild, hedgerow-fruit style and hints of pepper.

Malbec: Originally a Bordeaux variety, Malbec has become principally renowned in Argentina, where it thrives in the high-altitude vineyards of Mendoza. Wines are characterised by very dark, dense colour, and by aromas that perhaps fancifully evoke leather and liquorice as well as dark fruits. Flavours include black fruits with chocolate and spice; the wines are often grippy with retained tannin.

Merlot: Dark, rich colour. Aroma of sweet black cherry. Plummy, rich, mellow fruit can be akin to Cabernet but with less tannin. May be hints of bitter chocolate.

Pinot Noir: Colour distinctly pale, browning with age. Aromas of strawberry and raspberry. Light-bodied wine with soft-fruit flavours but dry, clean finish.

Sangiovese: The grape of Chianti and now of several other Italian regions, too. Colour is fine ruby, and may be relatively light; a plummy or even pruny smell is typical, and flavours can evoke blackcurrant, raspberry and nectarine. Tannin lingers, so the wine will have a dry, nutskin-like finish.

Shiraz or Syrah: Intense, near-black colour. Aroma of ripe fruit, sometimes spicy. Robust, rich flavours, commonly with high alcohol, but with soft tannins. The Shiraz of Australia is typically much more substantial than the Syrah of the south of France.

Tempranillo: Colour can be pale, as in Rioja. Blackcurrant aroma, often accompanied by vanilla from oak ageing. Tobacco, even leather, evoked in flavours.

There is more about all these varieties, and many others, in 'What wine words mean' starting on page 160.

Looking for a branded wine?

While the supermarkets' own-label wines – the likes of the Sainsbury's Taste the Difference and the Tesco Finest ranges – are obviously exclusive to the respective chains, branded wines are very often stocked by any number of different retailers.

If you're looking for a favourite brand, do check the index to this book on page 189. If I have tasted the wine and given it a mention, it is most likely to appear under the heading of the supermarket that hosted the tasting. But you might be accustomed to seeing this particular wine in another chain altogether.

I cannot give space in a pocket-sized book to repetitions of notes on popular brands that might very well be sold by each of the supermarket chains. But I do try to keep tasting the bestselling brands in hope of finding something positive to say about them.

Pick of the year:
—France forges ahead—

It's becoming a trend. In last year's edition of this book, I discovered to my surprise when the final reckoning of top-scoring wines was made, that nearly half the total turned out to be from France. This year, out of the 40 wines I have liked best of all, 21 are French. They've now gone beyond halfway.

It's quite striking. Most of the wines we buy to drink at home are in fact from Australia. France trails behind in terms of sheer quantity. But I have awarded top scores to only two Australian wines. What's going on? The answer is diversity. Nearly all the Aussie wines we drink in Britain are universal brands from the same ubiquitous grape varieties. They're great in their way, but they're awfully alike. In France, it's different. The wines are all over the place.

And there's a simpler explanation to the mystery too. Over a third of all the wines I have tasted for this book have been French. Fewer than a tenth have been Australian. Supermarkets might sell a lot of Aussie wines, but the choice that they offer from Down Under is narrow.

Looking at the wider picture, runner-up for top scores to France is Spain with a creditable eight. Next comes Italy with three, then South Africa, along with Australia, on two. Chile, England, New Zealand and the USA bring up the rear with one apiece.

The honours are rather more evenly distributed among the retailers. Waitrose is on top this year with eight. Sainsbury's follows up with six, just ahead of Asda, Majestic and Tesco with five each. The Co-op, Marks & Spencer and Morrisons all have three, and newcomer Lidl starts with two.

My top wines of the year

Red wines

The Wine Selection Côtes du Rhône 2012	Asda	£4.00
Tesco Beaujolais 2011	Tesco	£4.79
Cuvée Chasseur 2012	Waitrose	£4.99
Waitrose Soft and Juicy Chilean Red	Waitrose	£4.99
The Wine Selection Corbières 2012	Asda	£5.00
Cepa Lebrel Rioja Reserva 2008	Lidl	£5.99
Finest Côtes Catalanes Grenache 2012	Tesco	£6.99
Teroldego Rotaliano Riserva 2010	Lidl	£6.99
Zalze Shiraz Grenache Viognier 2011	Co-op	£7.99
Noster Nobilis Priorat 2009	Asda	£8.75
Château de L'Estaing 2010	Co-op	£8.99
Lirac Ogier La Marlerie 2011	Morrisons	£8.99
Château de Triniac 2011	Majestic	£9.99
Château La Tulipe de la Garde 2010	Sainsbury	£9.99
Georges Duboeuf Chiroubles 2011	Waitrose	£9.99

Kanonkop Kadette 2011	Sainsbury	£9.99
Taste the Difference Barbaresco 2009	Sainsbury	£9.99
Nicolas Potel Bourgogne Pinot Noir Vieilles Vignes 2011	Majestic	£11.99
Rioja Campo Aldea Graciano 2008	M&S	£12.99
Morellino di Scansano 2009	M&S	£15.99
Clos du Bois Sonoma Reserve Merlot 2009	Majestic	£18.99
Rioja Reserva Viña Ardanza 2004	Majestic	£22.00

White wines

The Wine Selection Marsanne 2012	Asda	£4.50
Waitrose Aromatic and Citrus Spanish Dry White 2012	Waitrose	£4.99
Finest St Mont 2011	Tesco	£6.99
The Wine Selection Chablis 2011	Asda	£7.75
Cave de Lugny Mâcon-Villages Chardonnay 2012	Waitrose	£7.99
Jean Biecher & Fils Pinot Gris Réserve 2011	Morrisons	£7.99
Taste the Difference Albariño Rias Baixas 2012	Sainsbury	£7.99
Bourgogne Chardonnay Les Chenaudières 2012	Majestic	£8.99
Taste the Difference Languedoc Blanc 2012	Sainsbury	£8.99

Emerald Cove Sauvignon Blanc 2012	M&S	£9.99
Taste the Difference Pouilly Fumé 2012	Sainsbury	£11.49
Tim Adams Clare Valley Semillon 2011	Tesco	£11.49
Jurançon Château Jolys Cuvée Jean 2010	Waitrose	£14.49
Wirra Wirra 12th Man Chardonnay 2011	Morrisons	£16.99

Fortified wine

Waitrose Amontillado Sherry	Waitrose	£6.99

Sparkling wines

Tesco Cava Brut	Tesco	£4.99
The Co-operative Les Pionniers Champagne Brut 2004	Co-op	£26.99
Camel Valley Pinot Noir Brut 2010	Waitrose	£27.99

Asda

If supermarkets could be said to have personalities – a laughable concept, I fully concede – I would count Asda as the most approachable and least daunting of the big chains.

It may be that the homely, budget-conscious theme of the corporate television advertising has been working on me. But it's probably the wines. I really like them. I find them appealing and uncomplicated, and they are good value.

This is particularly true of the own-label wines, which are arranged under two distinct headings. First is the Wine Selection, a newly defined range of what might be called 'everyday' wines at consumer-friendly prices. Then, upscale a bit, comes the Extra Special range, a much longer-established collection from all across the world of wine, at prices of £6 to £7 and upwards.

Each of these strands has its own merits, but I'll confess it's the Wine Selection that most impresses me this year. It's down, I believe, to the zeal of the company's wine manager, Philippa Carr. She is a Master of Wine, so she knows all about the world's grandest and most expensive wines. But in my chats with her at Asda tastings over the years I have also gathered that she has a special interest in finding wines of real quality and character at the humbler end of the scale.

'My job is to find wines for customers on every kind

of budget,' she tells me. 'Of course it's great to pick out fine wines that will appeal to shoppers looking for a special-occasion bottle, but it's obviously every bit as important to cater to people who really enjoy wine, but have only a fiver or so to spend. This is especially true these days, when a glass of wine is as much of a special treat as it's ever been.'

This chimes with the overall impression I get of Asda. Of course it's a huge monolithic beast, part of the world's biggest retailer, WalMart. But talking to someone as enthusiastic and dedicated as Philippa Carr is a reminder that however vast the supermarket chains are, they are still staffed by human beings. Just like you and me. I'll admit that in Philippa's case, she does have a knowledge and understanding of her subject that is quite beyond my ken, but at least she is deploying it in the interests of all of us.

RED WINES

ARGENTINA

 8 **The Wine Selection Argentinian Malbec 2012** £6.00

Lots of dark savour in this gamey blackberry meat-matcher made in Mendoza by Chile's Concha y Toro.

9 **Winemakers Shiraz 2011** £6.00

So pale it could be Pinot, but the raisiny, warmly spicy whiff tells otherwise; it's a vitally lively, healthy midweight red with pure-fruit virtue and unexpected allure; 14% alcohol.

8 **De Bortoli Family Selection Cabernet Merlot 2012** £7.00

Bordeaux-style grape blend from Riverina and King Valleys actually tastes rather Italian to me, even though the De Bortolis arrived in Oz (from Treviso) 85 years ago. Lovely perky berry-fruit red, refined and balanced.

8 **The Wine Selection Barossa Shiraz 2012** £7.00

Deep, dark and sinewy red-meat wine has a warming baked-fruit middle and nifty balance; 14% alcohol.

 8 **The Wine Selection Langhorne Creek Cabernet Sauvignon 2012** £7.00

Man's wine, this, if I dare say it, made suitably enough by a firm called Complexity Wines. It's an old-fashioned Aussie upfront Cabby with plenty of boot and 14% alcohol.

9 **De Bortoli Reserve Cabernet Sauvignon 2010** £9.99

Blended from Cabernet (and 6.7% Shiraz) from six different SE Australian locations, a lovely structured, luxuriously but discreetly oaked classic silky, cedary, cassis special-occasion red with 14.5% alcohol.

AUSTRALIA

RED WINES

Asda

CHILE

🍷 **8** **LFE Reserve Shiraz 2011** £6.00
Instantly appealing richly ripe and plausible bargain from
Luis Felipe Edwards; 14% alcohol.

🍷 **8** **Cono Sur Pinot Noir 2011** £7.50
Perpetual standby retains its familiar, warmly peppery
cherry-raspberry fruit with plenty of substance.

FRANCE

🍷 **10** **The Wine Selection Côtes du Rhône 2012** £4.00
I had to take the £4 price with a pinch of salt, but otherwise
this sunny red tastes of nothing but pure, convincing joy.
By regional giant Cellier des Dauphins, it's pale but not
wan in colour, has a super berry-pepper nose, and cheery,
healthy, spicy-fresh authentic CdR fruit.

🍷 **9** **The Wine Selection Syrah 2012** £4.75
Asda source a lot of wine from Foncalieu, a big Languedoc
co-op, and a very wise policy it is too. This purple-black,
jammy-nosed but ideally poised spicy, warming, fleshy
juice bomb is phenomenal value at the price.

🍷 **8** **The Wine Selection Claret 2012** £5.00
Cheap claret rarely holds out much hope, but here's a
really decent Merlot-led, brambly-leafy, pure-tasting and
satisfying one for a fiver.

🍷 **10** **The Wine Selection Corbières 2012** £5.00
This is fantastically good, from a Mediterranean AC not
always known for excellence. It's inky, deeply intense,
blackberry-pure and balanced, finishing perfectly clean.
The price looks like a misprint and I reckon this will
improve for a year or two.

RED WINES

FRANCE

8 **The Wine Selection Beaujolais 2011** £5.50
Purple bouncy-juicy quaffer even has a citrus edge; full
of life even though 2011 (2012 might not be such fun).

8 **La Vieille Ferme 2012** £6.75
Chickens on the label always does it for me, but this
popular Ventoux brand by the Perrins of Châteauneuf du
Pape is well-placed in the pecking order: comforting, ripe,
peppery red with Grenache spice and Syrah slickness,
with 14% alcohol.

8 **Extra Special Cabernet Sauvignon 2011** £7.25
Dramatically deep-purple Languedoc juicy-minty plush
blackcurrant Cabernet is gently gripping, with 14%
alcohol.

9 **Extra Special Corbières 2011** £7.25
From the same source (Foncalieu) as the revelatory Wine
Selection Corbières above, this is sleek from oak contact,
a nice dark and spicy smoothie with definition.

8 **Le Grand Clauzy Merlot 2012** £7.25
It has that intriguing southern garrigue savour as well as
the bright morello cherry charm from Merlot grapes; nice
plump-but-crisp summer red; 14% alcohol.

8 **The Original Malbec 2012** £7.25
The name references the regional origin of this easy-to-
like savoury red, the Lot Valley, home of the mythical
'black wine' of Cahors, made from Malbec grapes. This
is not particularly black and indeed has a light touch, but
plenty of sinewy, roasty Malbec fruit.

RED WINES

FRANCE

🍷 8 **Le Manoir du Baron Pinot Noir 2012**   £7.75
Foncalieu (ace Languedoc co-op) warm-weather Pinot is
edgy with nice crunchy summer soft-fruit juiciness; drink
this cool.

🍷 8 **Château St Germain 2011**   £8.25
Merlot-Cabernet formula Entre-Deux-Mers (Bordeaux
boondocks) red by Calvet is roasty-ripe with a bitter-
chocolate centre; tastes better than I make it sound, on
reflection.

🍷 8 **Grignan Les Aldhémar 2011**   £8.50
The name is that of a mystery appellation in the Rhône
and the wine is a conventional Grenache-Syrah blend
with muscular spicy black fruit, and some distinction,
maybe a bit like Vacqueyras. Try it.

🍷 8 **Extra Special Châteauneuf du Pape 2011**   £13.50
Friendly, agreeably nuanced example of the Rhône's
flagship red is not ludicrously overpriced (like some), and
is 14.5% alcohol.

ITALY

🍷 8 **The Wine Selection Sicilian Red 2012**   £4.25
Lightish herby-cherry-scented fresh glugger largely from
Sangiovese (Chianti) grapes has warm Sicilian charm.

🍷 8 **Casa Lella Barbera 2011**   £6.00
From reliable Piedmont outfit Araldica, a bouncing
brambly Barbera d'Asti with masses of juicy fruit.

🍷 8 **Extra Special Primitivo 2010**   £7.00
Can you say a wine evokes a volcano? If so, this dark and
fiery Puglian barbecue red does, with its suggestions of
bushy-briar fruit grown on brimstone slopes.

8 **Extra Special Montepulciano d'Abruzzo 2011 £7.00**
Within the limitations of what Montepulciano grapes
grown in the Abruzzo can do, this isn't bad; vigorous
dry-finishing sweet-briar pasta red with vanilla from oak.

9 **Extra Special Barbera 2011** **£8.00**
I decided after long contemplation that this is, after all,
extra special. It might just be the creamy suggestion of
oak in the dark, juicy, crunchy-blueberry fruit, but I am
completely taken in; another Araldica wine, with 14.5%
alcohol.

9 **Extra Special Chianti Classico Riserva 2009 £9.00**
I liked this best of all the Asda Chiantis, but it's the
priciest; dark, dense and exotic, with heaps of black-
cherry savour, but finely poised and brisk with a proper
drying nutskin finish.

8 **Extra Special Valpolicella Ripasso 2010** **£9.00**
Now-ubiquitous Veronese plumped-up speciality red is
irresistible, especially when as velvety and rich as this one.

9 **Extra Special New Zealand Pinot Noir 2011 £11.00**
Big strawberry nose on this warmly ripe Marlborough
pale red from Wither Hills winery has burgundian-style
oaked slinky sleekness. Kiwi Pinot merits its growing cult
status.

8 **Wishbone Pinot Noir 2011** **£11.00**
Pale limpid leafy defined pure stony-bright Pinot of
elegant weight from fancifully named Mount Olympus
winery in Marlborough is worth the money.

RED WINES

ROMANIA

8 Bradshaw Pinot Noir 2012 £6.00
Such an odd package, but a likeable ripe cherry-strawberry
Pinot of character, with a silky texture.

SOUTH AFRICA

8 Extra Special South African Pinotage 2012 £7.00
Pinotage is a quirky grape unique to the Cape, making
strong, tarry reds you either like or don't. I like this
one's juicy-spicy savour and distinctive pungency; 14.5%
alcohol.

8 De Bos Shiraz 2011 £8.50
Whole basket of berry fruits in this sunny Fairtrade wine,
tasting rounded and balanced with 14% alcohol.

**8 The Wine Selection Marques del Norte
Rioja Joven 2012** £5.00
'Young' (joven) Rioja without oak contact has sunny,
plump raspberry-blackcurrant fruit and a creaminess that
does, oddly enough, suggest an acquaintance with the old
quercus; 14% alcohol.

SPAIN

**8 The Wine Selection Garnacha Tempranillo
2012** £5.25
Sweet hint of syrup is firmly defrayed by the brisk finish
on this spicy Valencian blend; good chilli partner, with
14% alcohol.

8 Extra Special Old Vines Garnacha 2012 £8.25
The vines are 25 years old, as if you care. The wine is
a mature-tasting substantial ripe mélange of deep berry
fruits with dark richness and 14% alcohol, from the
Cariñena region.

RED WINES

SPAIN

🍷 **8 Paul de Albas Ribero del Duero 2012**   £8.25
Nice example of what one heretic I know likes to call
Ribena del Duero, because these wines can have a lot
of sweet blackcurrant fruit. This does so, from 100%
Tempranillo grapes, but also has the hallmark slick
eucalypt focus in the dark fruit, and lovely balance.

🍷 **10 Noster Nobilis Priorat 2009**   £8.75
Last year I gave the 2007 a top score, and likewise this
lovely gamey Garnacha-Carignan blend of toasty-oaked
pitchy-savoury briar fruits from the fabled Priorat
vineyards at an exceptionally keen price; 14.5% alcohol.

PINK WINES

FRANCE

🍷 **7 Les Estivales Rosé 2012**   £6.75
Pale magenta Languedoc pink has a strawberry note,
fleeting spritz and easy acidity.

SPAIN

🍷 **8 Pelayo Rosé 2012**   £7.25
Bright in colour and fruit, a firmly dry redcurranty
refresher from Navarra with a bit of woof.

WHITE WINES

AUSTRALIA

🍷 8 **De Bortoli Family Selection Chardonnay 2012** £7.00
Cool, crisp, but craftily creamy dry Riverina wine has very likeable apple-strudel contrasts.

🍷 8 **The Wine Selection Margaret River Semillon Sauvignon 2012** £7.00
Interesting gooseberry-pineapple style to a fresh tangy dry wine with a long lick of tropical fruit, made by an outfit called Complexity Wines.

CHILE

🍷 8 **Mayu Pedro Ximenez 2012** £7.00
Pale dry white from a grape otherwise known only as the sweetening variety for sherry. It conjures up ripe greenhouse fruits and yet is breezily brisk and fresh.

🍷 8 **LFE Seleccion De Familia Sauvignon Blanc 2012** £7.50
Powerful asparagus pong is followed up by crisp, new-mown-grass freshness and long fruit; made by Luis Felipe Edwards.

FRANCE

🍷 8 **The Wine Selection Chardonnay 2012** £4.50
Languedoc (Foncalieu co-operative) device is apple-fresh with a crafty lick of residual sugar. Bargain.

🍷 10 **The Wine Selection Marsanne 2012** £4.50
Brilliant successor to the 10-scoring 2011, this alluringly coloured lovely fruit-salad ensemble from Foncalieu in the Languedoc balances fresh, tangy zest with glorious orchard-exotic white fruits to miraculous effect at a ridiculously low price.

WHITE WINES

7 Kiwi Cuvée Sauvignon Blanc 2012   £6.25
It was sporting of the French to award this a gold medal in
the Anivin competition. It's a simple Loire wine nothing
like its New Zealand counterparts.

**8 Château Salmonière Muscadet de Sèvre
et Maine 2012**   £6.50
Bracing bone-dry Loire-estuary shellfish wine with lots of
briny fruit and not too much greenness; leesy intensity as
hoped for in a 'sur lie' wine.

8 Extra Special Viognier 2012   £7.00
Languedoc dry white has signature apricot character of
Viognier grape with a nifty dry-but-creamy poise. Cold
roast chicken wine, if you get my drift.

8 Etoile de Nuit Sauvignon Blanc 2012   £7.50
For an anonymous Languedoc wine this looks expensive,
but there's a lot of racing, grassy lushness and full,
impactful classy Sauvignon fruit here, and a textbook
tangy edge.

8 Le Manoir Du Baron Chardonnay 2012   £7.75
Lazily named but cleverly made Languedoc dry wine by
Foncalieu rather in the Mâconnais style has long-but-
fresh sweet-apple fruit.

10 The Wine Selection Chablis 2011   £7.75
Ooh, this is good. First whiff is pure stony-twangy-lifted
ripe apple uniquely Chablis Chardonnay, delightfully so.
Upfront fruit and citrus edge. Top value too.

WHITE WINES

FRANCE

8 Extra Special Alsace Gewürztraminer 2011 £8.00
From, almost inevitably, the Turckheim co-operative, it's
quite sweet, but I still liked it; big lychee honk and a lot
of fresh pineapple in the long, spicy flavours.

**9 Extra Special Chablis Domaine de la Levée
2011 £9.50**
Richly coloured, typically lush style from Chablis legend
Jean-Marc Brocard is an artful contrivance indeed.
Delicious and good value.

8 Extra Special Pouilly Fumé 2012 £11.00
Famed Loire Sauvignon is as nettly, stony, river-fresh and
burbling with grassy fruit as you would expect for the
outlay; 14% alcohol.

8 Extra Special Sancerre 2012 £11.50
Flinty-leesy and reasonably priced example of the Loire
classic, made by respected Joseph Mellot (who also does
the Pouilly Fumé for Asda).

ITALY

9 The Wine Selection Soave 2012 £4.25
Nice twang of lemon zing on the edge of this bright
orchard-fruit Verona dry white in which a little bit
of creamy blanched-almond richness flickers; 11.5%
alcohol. Very keen price for this quality.

7 The Wine Selection Pinot Grigio 2012 £4.50
Sweet pear fruit bunches up at the back of the flavour, but
at least it tastes of something. Fair price.

WHITE WINES

8 Lugana 2012 £8.50
Lush Lake Garda dry white is herbaceous, peachy and
evocatively sun-ripened; it's quite rich, but uplifts to a
twangy lemon finish.

7 Garganega Pouch 2012 £9.50
Yes, you read it right; it's a 1.5-litre boxless bag containing
wine from a grape called Garganega. And it's not bad,
a bit like Soave, the dry white Verona wine made from
Garganega.

**8 The Wine Selection New Zealand
Sauvignon Blanc 2012** £6.25
Familiar peapod Kiwi style to this conventional but jolly
refreshing and grassy Marlborough dry wine at a keen
price.

**9 Extra Special New Zealand
Sauvignon Blanc 2012** £9.00
I don't care if it's a cliché, this brisk gooseberry-juicy,
beany-grassy, even minty extravagance of glittering green
fruit is an absolute joy; made by Wither Hills.

**8 Villa Maria Private Bin Sauvignon Blanc
2012** £10.00
It might seem spartan by some Kiwi standards, but it's
vitally refreshing, with a sneaky hint of raspberry amid
the seagrass and sunshine.

8 Bradshaw Pinot Grigio 2012 £6.00
Don't let the disorientating label put you off; this
generously fruity, smoky and aromatic PG is closer in
style and interest to Alsace than it is to dreary old Veneto.

WHITE WINES

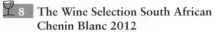

SOUTH AFRICA

🍷 8 **The Wine Selection South African
Chenin Blanc 2012**   £5.00
Perfectly dry, which is unusual for Chenin Blanc, this has
fresh green appeal; good-value summer party white.

🍷 8 **Extra Special South African Chenin Blanc
2012**   £7.00
More typical and quite delicious, this is finely balanced,
crisp and vivacious with a natural richness; 14% alcohol.

SPARKLING WINES

FRANCE

8 **Louvel Fontaine Champagne Brut** £24.25
Respectable full-of-fruit crisp fizz has been discounted to
£12, which makes it a genuine bargain.

8 **Extra Special Louis Bernard Vintage**
Champagne 2004 £25.25
New house vintage champagne is mellow and developed,
with yeasty richness.

8 **Bollinger Special Cuvée** £42.00
I'm grateful to Asda for including this prestige champagne
marque in the tasting; fine lemon-gold colour, big assertive
lemon-cream biscuit style; lovely fizz at an outrageous
price.

SPAIN

8 **The Wine Selection Cava Brut** £5.25
Asda has a knack with cava, and this bargain is well up
to snuff, with floral scent, busy froth, quite dry and fresh
crisp-pear fruit; 11.5% alcohol.

8 **Extra Special Rosé Vintage Cava Brut 2010** £8.25
Luminous strawberry fizz is fresh, perky and fun.

The Co-operative

The Co-op is everywhere. With six million card-carrying members among its countless customers, the network has grown to more than 3,000 food outlets around the country – no other retailer comes close – and all of them, as far as I know, sell wine.

Of course, some of the stores offer more of a choice than others. In the little convenience stores that account for most of the network, you can choose among a few dozen bottles at what might be called everyday prices. In recent years, however, the Co-op wine department has been moving upmarket. There are now more than 400 shops, nationwide, designated 'Fine Wine' outlets.

Here you'll find a range that runs into the hundreds, starting with those everyday reds and whites (some of them very good and good value), then rising gradually through a sensibly graded price scale into the proverbial fine-wine realm.

I have tasted some of the new wines and new vintages lately added to the range at each level, and can report that the choice at the Co-op continues to grow impressively. And while other major chains have been experiencing a slide in wine sales, in 2012 the Co-op set a new record for turnover, up £10 million on the previous year.

Consistency of quality is similarly on the up. There are wines here I would be pleased to find in any retail multiple, let alone one as down-to-earth as the Co-op. There is real expertise among the buyers who seek out the range.

RED WINES

ARGENTINA

🍷 8 **Vinalba Patagonian Cabernet Merlot 2010 £9.99**
Inky dark-purple Bordeaux-type blend is grippingly ripe
but by no means frazzled; a big savoury meat-matcher
with 14.5% alcohol.

🍷 8 **Jim Barry The Lodge Hill Shiraz 2012 £9.99**
Vigorous, callow-coloured Clare Valley baked-fish wine
has briar-blackberry bounce, sunny spice and friendly
grab-you-by-the-chops tannins.

AUSTRALIA

🍷 8 **The Lioness Shiraz 2009 £10.99**
Colour is already browning in this ripely rich, spirity-
nosed roast-beef red in genteel decay; a rarely mature
wine with warm spice, retreating tannins and 14.5%
alcohol.

🍷 8 **Wirra Wirra Church Block Cabernet
Shiraz Merlot 2011 £12.99**
Purple depths and pruny-liquorice savour in this richly
oaked McLaren Vale icon wine make for an awesome
mouthful; it has an elegant weight, though, for all its
14.5% alcohol.

CHILE

🍷 8 **Cono Sur Bicicleta Pinot Noir 2012 £7.49**
Stalwart sweetly oaked cherry warm-weather Pinot of
clean appeal.

🍷 8 **Montgras Reserva Carmenère 2012 £9.99**
Carmine colour gives the grape its name in this bright
blackcurrant oaked red with a hint of butterscotch; 14%
alcohol.

RED WINES

8 Ogier Côtes du Rhône Réserve 2011   £6.99
Scorched centre to the pitch-dark fruit is intriguing in this
spicy middleweight. Nice match for warming chilli dishes.

8 Château Sainte Marthe 2011   £7.99
This Syrah-Grenache blend immediately reveals
Mediterranean credentials with its warmly spicy and
intense black-fruit nose; the flavours follow up well.

10 Château de L'Estaing 2010   £8.99
Perfectly pitched claret from the fabled 2010 vintage is
now spot on; slinky, well-evolved black-cherry and fleshy
blackcurrant fruits artfully oaked. From the remote and
undervalued Côtes de Castillon appellation, it has 14%
alcohol. Top bargain.

8 Jour de Nuit Cabernet Merlot 2011   £9.99
The arty label is a bit much, though I like the uncomplicated
juicy fruit blend, which has a claret-like elegance but is in
fact from the Languedoc.

**9 Pic St Loup Domaine Les Grandes Costes
2009**   £13.99
Fine example of a buzzy red from the Languedoc is a
deliciously intense and developed Syrah-Grenache mix
with notions of raisin, liquorice, black pepper and the
mysterious garrigue. Gorgeous wine that will be in short
supply; 14.5% alcohol.

9 Château Sénéjac 2009   £16.99
Famous Haut-Médoc estate made a sublime wine in this
legendary vintage, now coming round nicely with proper
tobacco-cedar whiffs and rich cassis fruit; lovely claret at
a perfectly fair price.

RED WINES

ITALY

8 Casa Planeta Nero d'Avola Syrah 2012 £8.99
Savoury Sicilian blend quite elegantly delivers defined black fruits and a clean, dry exit. Simply likeable.

8 Villa Annaberta Amarone della Valpolicella 2009 £16.99
Fine example of Verona's monster red has brooding ruby depths and near-raisiny ripe darkness of fruit; intensely rich but finishing properly 'amarone' (bitter), with coffee notes and 15% alcohol.

N. ZEALAND

9 Waipara Hills Pinot Noir 2011 £12.99
Strawberries and cream are pleasingly evoked in this lush, smooth and eucalypt-minty part-oaked Central Otago summer red; classic Kiwi Pinot with 14% alcohol.

SOUTH AFRICA

8 The Co-operative South African Cabernet Sauvignon 2012 £5.75
Friendly, ripe-blackcurrant 'lightly oaked' party red with 14% alcohol.

9 Paarl Mountains Cabernet 2011 £6.99
Instantly likeable, sweetly spicy, cleverly weighted black-fruit food red delivers a lot of richness and concentration for the money; 14% alcohol.

8 Railroad Red 2010 £6.99
Complicated oaked blend of seven different grapes led by Syrah has simple enough appeal: brightly fruity, substantial, spicy and long, with 14% alcohol.

RED WINES

SOUTH AFRICA

10 Zalze Shiraz Grenache Viognier 2011 £7.99
The Kleine Zalze estate a mile or so from Stellenbosch
has been making wine since 1695 and is now also a major
tourist attraction, complete with golf course. But that
doesn't stop them making fabulous wine. With intense
flavours and keen definition in ideal balance, this actually
lives up to the back-label claim of 'black-olive fruit'.
Outstanding value; 14.5% alcohol.

**9 Vergelegen Cabernet Sauvignon Reserve
2006** £13.99
Browning bricky-ruby, long-oak-aged Bordeaux-style
wine from a revered estate has a cryptic Cabernet nose,
finely poised, near-austere cedar-cassis fruit and a lot of
class; 14% alcohol.

SPAIN

8 Pago de Los Capellanes Crianza 2009 £17.99
Serious deep-purple pure Tempranillo from Ribera del
Duero is still a bit treacly and grabby with tannin, but
will be massively good in a few years, if you have the
patience as well as the pesetas.

WHITE WINES

ARGENTINA

🍷 8 **The Co-operative Fairtrade Torrontes-
Chardonnay 2012**   **£4.99**
Grapy-honeysuckle nose on this fresh and interesting
muscatty aperitif blend.

AUSTRALIA

🍷 8 **Signal Post Chardonnay 2012**   **£7.49**
Toffee-apple style, though no oak, in this ripe-but-brisk
Chardy with a tiny dollop of softening Viognier in it.

🍷 8 **Eltzinger Grüner Veltliner 2012**   **£8.99**
Florally perfumed dry white so fresh there's a ghost of
spritz to it; distinctive aperitif wine with exotic white fruit
and a pinch of white pepper.

🍷 7 **Yalumba Y Series Pinot Grigio 2012**   **£8.99**
PG fans should try this Aussie spin on the Italian original;
this has lots of aromatic fruit, a whiff of wood smoke and
not a lot of acidity.

🍷 8 **Jim Barry The Lodge Hill Riesling 2012**   **£9.99**
Proper limey, long-flavoured, dry, palate-thrilling Aussie
Riesling from a great winery in the Clare Valley.

FRANCE

🍷 8 **Calvet Limited Release Sauvignon Blanc
2012**   **£6.99**
One of the better mass-market dry white Bordeaux brands
of 2012, this has racy green freshness and plenty of fruit.

🍷 9 **Château de la Petite Giraudière Muscadet de
Sèvre et Maine Sur Lie 2012**   **£6.99**
You get a proper briny blast of the seafront – the Atlantic
seafront, no less – from this bracing, fruit-packed and
convincing Loire-estuary classic. Really terrific.

WHITE WINES

GERMANY

🍷 9 **Reichsgraf von Kesselstatt Riesling Kabinett 2011** £9.99
Generous, racy, lush moselle has a seductive trace of honey en route to the freshest, tangiest of finishes; 10% alcohol.

ITALY

🍷 8 **Casa Planeta Grecanico Chardonnay 2012** £8.99
Stirring pong of brassica from the Grecanico in this Sicilian admixture balances the peachiness of the Chardonnay to make a dry, refreshing and contemplative whole.

NEW ZEALAND

🍷 9 **The Co-operative Explorers Marlborough Sauvignon Blanc 2012** £8.99
Very consistent Co-op standby has masses of asparagus-nettle interest and lush grassy freshness; well-made wine in which the flavours go all the way through.

🍷 8 **The Co-operative Premium Marlborough Pinot Grigio 2012** £9.99
Aromatic dry wine has interesting grapefruit and broad bean notions about it (or maybe I imagined them) amounting to an alluring overall effect. Asian food or charcuterie.

🍷 9 **Peter Yealands Sauvignon Blanc 2012** £9.99
Asparagus nose and top fruit in this distinctive, long-flavoured and intense Marlborough wine out of the top drawer.

WHITE WINES

SOUTH AFRICA

7 Stonehaven Sauvignon Blanc 2012 £7.99
Straight, grassy, typical Cape variation on the global Sauvignon theme has a lick of sweetness which some will like better than others.

8 Rustenberg SWB 2011 £9.99
I found apples, pears, peaches and nectarines in this basket of ripe fruits; decent oaked mainly Semillon-Viognier blend with 14.5% alcohol.

SPARKLING WINES

FRANCE

**9 The Co-operative Les Pionniers
Champagne Brut** £19.99
Lovable rich-tea biscuit nose and long tangy developed fruit with fleeting strawberry perfume in this classy non-vintage; the name Pionniers is French for Pioneers, as in the Rochdale Pioneers who founded the Co-operative Movement.

**10 The Co-operative Les Pionniers
Champagne Brut 2004** £26.99
Fabled vintage own brand has the goldening colour of bottle age, buttered-toast perfume, expensive tight mousse, mellow, mature, glitteringly highlighted flavours; grand by any standard, it's made by Piper Heidsieck.

ITALY

8 The Co-operative Prosecco £9.99
Sweet pear nose, busy foam, perky near-dry fresh orchardy fruit. Good one.

Lidl

Welcome to Lidl, a newcomer to these pages. I have been trying wines from this 600-branch 'no-frills' chain for years, but until this year have found too few interesting items to constitute an entry here. But now, Lidl UK has launched its 'first ever premium wine range in response to growing demand for fine wines from affluent but spend-savvy customers'.

Well, that's what the press announcement said. It added that £1 million has been spent on kitting out all the stores with new displays for the 'Wine Cellar' range, as the new upmarket wines are collectively known. There have been a score of so them introduced so far, and I have tasted most of them.

Of those, a dozen appear here for the straightforward reason that they are good and good value, and in some cases jolly good and jolly interesting, too. I look forward to the range growing, and maybe even to some developments among the more everyday wines. Watch this space.

And meanwhile, let me give space to Lidl's Specialist Wine Category Manager Ben Hulme's message about this new move: 'We believe in offering affordable luxury to everyone, and this Wine Cellar is a true extension of that. We're wanting to offer people the opportunity to enjoy really good wines at prices that aren't ridiculous. Since the recession hit, we've seen a shift in customer spending habits, with many people, even those from more affluent backgrounds, finding smart ways to continue enjoying fine wines and good food at home. The Lidl Wine Cellar allows you to do just that.'

RED WINES

ARGENTINA

8 **Mendoza Malbec 2012** £5.99

Balanced purple-ruby food wine has trace of leather in the blueberry nose, in true Malbec style, and the fruit is healthy with a touch of sweetness. Good match for chilli dishes.

9 **Vacqueyras 2011** £7.99

Spot-on southern Rhône appellation from a vintage as ripe as the yummily roasted core of fruit revealed in this intense, spicy wine. A thoroughly solid Vacqueyras, at a very respectable price.

FRANCE

7 **Châteauneuf du Pape 2011** £12.49

Inexpensive by prevailing standards, this is lighter in weight and density than might be expected, though 14% alcohol.

9 **Château Laroze 2007** £19.99

It's a grand cru classé of St Emilion, and this is what you'd expect to pay for it, even at Lidl. This is a modern claret, soupy and dark, plump with very ripe cherry and redcurrant fruit, enriched with new(ish) oak contact, and to me, tasting younger than its years. A proper wine to drink or keep.

ITALY

10 **Teroldego Rotaliano Riserva 2010** £6.99

This is absolutely terrific, an esoteric red from sub-alpine Italy with unique characteristics of black-fruit savour, eager ripeness and delectable, green-tinged, food-flattering abrasion; it's a riserva wine with some oak ageing and has a mellow maturity as well as a perfect dry balance.

RED WINES

ITALY

🍷 6 **Rosso di Montalcino 2010** £9.99
Disappointing. I've included it because it's a big, liquorous wine but too sweet and not enough like the distinctive slinky-minty super-Chianti style of Montalcino.

SPAIN

🍷 10 **Cepa Lebrel Rioja Reserva 2008** £5.99
The best-value Rioja I have found in a long while is mellow in years, with the deliciously decadent aroma of extra-ripe strawberries and raspberries that these wines give off with age. And the fruit here is highlighted rather than stifled by the vanilla oak. In short, brilliant, and at Lidl's price, a rare bargain.

🍷 8 **Saxa Loquuntur Rioja 2011** £6.99
Vivid and juicy young Rioja whose curious name translates roughly as 'the stones are talking' – i.e. the ground speaks to you though the wine. Fanciful but fun.

WHITE WINES

FRANCE

9 Gros Plant du Pays Nantais 2012   **£5.99**

An esoteric Loire-estuary wine known, if at all, as the most astringent dry white of France. But this one is positively friendly, bone-dry but with plenty of crisp white fruit, briny freshness and neat balance; it grows on you and the price is very keen; 10.5% alcohol.

9 Chablis 2012   **£7.69**

I liked this at once because it smells and tastes just like Chablis. You can't say that of every wine so called at under a tenner, believe me. It has the right flinty aroma, oyster-shell minerality and sunny-ripe-but-lemon-edged Chardonnay fruit. Spot on.

8 Sancerre Comte d'Ardières 2012   **£9.99**

Sancerre, the grandest Loire appellation for Sauvignon Blanc, is not much found for under a tenner; this one is true to style, with a gunflint whiff, grassy rush of fruit and tangy (if softer than some) acidity.

ITALY

8 Grillo Terre Siciliane 2012   **£5.99**

Almondy perfume with an intriguing petrol note and green orchard fruit in attention-grabbing counterpoint here. It's a big-flavoured, herbaceous-citrus wine to match fish or poultry.

SPARKLING WINE

9 **Comte de Brismand Champagne Brut**   £12.99
Absolutely decent lemony-fresh and authentic non-vintage
champagne at a low, low price which has occasionally
been lowered even further.

Majestic

 There is no other wine merchant like Majestic. This is a continuing source of wonder to me, because the formula that this enterprising retailer uses seems to be simplicity itself.

It's like this. You buy or rent a decent-sized empty building and fill it with wine. No shelves, racks or other fripperies. Just stacks and stacks of cases, with the loose bottles wobbling about on top. You insist that customers buy at least six bottles (it used to be 12) at a time, any mix, and provide supermarket trolleys for them to load their purchases into as they trundle up and down the canyons of cases. You offer discounts on most of the wines, on the basis of 'buy two bottles, save 20 per cent'. As there is a minimum purchase anyway, it's a no-brainer.

You also provide handy, free parking, and the staff – invariably friendly, knowledgeable, enthusiastic and physically robust – will load the case or cases into the back of your car. Shopping for wine in Majestic is easy, fun, even quite sociable.

The wines are different from those in the supermarkets. There's more choice – more of the wines come from small producers whose scale doesn't suit the supermarkets. You see? It's so simple. Why doesn't everybody else who wishes to sell wine do it the way Majestic does? Well, they don't. More's the pity. But at least Majestic are doing it, and prospering mightily. Long may it last.

Just a word about the prices in the following pages. Most of them are likely to be 20 per cent above what you'll actually pay, because of the high proportion of wines always on multibuy offer. I confess I have had this likely price adjustment in the back of my mind when scoring the wines. My troubles is that I can't believe anybody buys any wine from Majestic that isn't on discount. So where you see an implausible price such as £8.74, think of it really at a fifth less – the rather more familiar figure of £6.99. And so on.

As for the wines, they're as good as ever, especially from Burgundy and southwest France, Italy, Rioja, even (from time to time) Germany. You don't have to visit the stores in person to shop. You can look at the current list on the website (or download it) and order either online or, if you're a dinosaur in this field of endeavour, phone up your local outlet and reel off your requirements; they'll then deliver it in one of their little vans. Minimum order for home delivery, by the way, is 12 bottles. Just like in the old days.

RED WINES

ARGENTINA

🍷 **8** **Callia Bella Malbec 2012** £8.99
Amiable deep-purple San Juan wine has a whiff of syrup
but a firm, agreeably peppery grip; 14% alcohol.

🍷 **8** **Septimo Dia Malbec 2010** £9.99
You get the 'leather' aroma and savour for which
Argentine Malbec is famous/infamous in this, plus plenty
of dark, even brûlée, spicy briar fruit; good, interesting
red with 14% alcohol.

🍷 **9** **DB Reserve Pinot Noir 2011** £9.99
Pale, pretty-coloured, earthy, naturally pure-tasting,
outdoorsy-fresh, delicious cool-climate-style Pinot of
great character from Victoria-based De Bortoli family
winery. Exceptional.

AUSTRALIA

🍷 **8** **Wirra Wirra Church Block Cabernet
Shiraz Merlot 2010** £12.49
Dense, spicy barbecue red has warm savour of sleek oak
contact and 14.5% alcohol. More mellow than the 2011,
as stocked by the Co-op.

🍷 **8** **Two Hands Angels' Share Shiraz 2011** £22.00
Very deep-purple long lush premium McLaren Vale wine
has deep blackberries-with-cream fruit and confidently
orchestrated flavours with 14.5% alcohol. For special
Aussie occasions; nice arty label too.

CHILE

🍷 **9** **Mister Shiraz 2011** £8.74
No prizes for the name but it has a sumptuous purple
colour, and exactly the kind of generous sweetly ripe fruit
for which Chile is so admired; deep, minty-spicy food
wine for roasts and stews; 14% alcohol.

RED WINES

8 **Bordeaux Supérieur Lacroix 2007** £7.99
Mature modern claret, browning at the edge, has a sweet
cedar nose and plump, long Merlot fruit.

8 **Paul Mas Merlot 2012** £7.99
Simple baked summer-fruit-tart Pays d'Oc is generous
with ripe black-cherry juiciness.

8 **Pennautier Cabernet Sauvignon 2012** £7.99
Blatant blackberry fruit in this lively, grippy young Pays
d'Oc.

9 **Beaujolais Domaine de la Motte 2011** £8.74
Unusually plump and velvety style from vineyards at
Brouilly (a cru known for fuller wines), nevertheless
bright with juicy raspberry and cherry fruits; stands out,
and might last.

8 **Beaujolais-Villages Georges Duboeuf 2011** £8.74
In the absence of 2012 wines, a firm, crunchy and lively
Beaujolais with grip and freshness; hope it lasts.

9 **Domaine Les Yeuses Les Epices Syrah 2010** £8.99
Exotic, exciting chocolate-mint nose on this crimson
smoothie leads into rich spicy fruit of sinewy body and
profound depth; from a mature and wondrous vintage in
the Languedoc.

8 **L'Instant Truffier Malbec 2012** £8.99
From Cahors producer St Didier Parnac, a big, dark,
spicy and rich red from the local grape under the generic
Côtes du Lot classification; as good as most Cahors, but
no sign of truffles.

FRANCE

RED WINES

10 Château de Triniac 2011   £9.99
From the not-much-evident appellation of Côtes du
Roussillon Villages, this theatrically rich and opulent
Carignan-Syrah-Grenache blend simply hits the spot
with its gorgeous limpid spicy-garrigue black fruits and
surpassing sleekness with 14.5% alcohol. Good advice on
the back label: decant it.

8 Châteaux l'Abbaye de Sainte-Ferme 2005   £9.99
From a famed and now mellow Bordeaux vintage, this
is engagingly ripe, deep and developed with a Rioja-like
creaminess; 14% alcohol.

8 Côtes du Rhône Belleruche 2011   £9.99
Top-drawer wine from Rhône biodynamic maestro
Chapoutier is sleek, spicy and concentrated but with
perky blackberry brightness besides; 14% alcohol.

8 Morgon Château de Pizay 2011   £10.49
This Beaujolais cru from a wondrously good vintage is
a wine to keep; the fruit is bright and juicy but tight and
tannic, too; it could well turn into a classic a couple of
years hence.

9 La Granges des Combes 2011   £10.99
From the Roquebrun co-op at St Chinian in the
Languedoc, this Syrah-Grenache-Mourvèdre blend is
deep crimson, with an alluring spicy-truffly nose and the
distinct burnt-earth briary-black fruitiness of the best St
Chinian; a generous, standout winter warmer with 14%
alcohol.

FRANCE

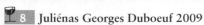

RED WINES

🍷 8 Juliénas Georges Duboeuf 2009   £11.24

Serious Beaujolais and a serious price, this maturing cru is taking on the firm, cherry nuances of the grander style of red burgundy (made from Pinot Noir, not Gamay as in Beaujolais); fascinating and delightful.

🍷 10 Nicolas Potel Bourgogne Pinot Noir
Vieilles Vignes 2011   £11.99

This is the sort of wine that gives Burgundy a good name. Nicolas Potel (or his successor, as he's just retired) is a genius, and this pale but hugely ripe cherry-raspberry exquisitely defined Pinot is a tour de force, silkily creamy but piquantly fresh, all at the same time.

🍷 8 Bellero Barbera 2012   £7.49

Piedmont juicy red's as bouncy as its name might intimate, but intense and deep, too, with the grip of an extra-ripe year.

🍷 9 Casa d'Aragona Salice Salentino 2010   £8.74

Plausible – no, better than that, adorable – southern Negroamaro has roast-fruit savour, cherry plumpness, volcanic ardour; what's not to like?

🍷 8 Surani Costarossa Primitivo di Manduria
2011   £9.99

From Puglia in Italy's heel, a deep-crimson monster with figgy wafts and roasted brambly savour; 14.5% alcohol.

🍷 8 Chianti Classico San Leonino 2009   £10.61

High-toned, sweetly ripe riserva with bright briar fruit dusted with white pepper.

FRANCE

ITALY

Majestic

RED WINES

ITALY

8 **Spolverino Toscano Carpineto 2011**   £12.49
Coffee and dark chocolate in the depths of this gripping Chianti-style elegantly balanced fruit-and-nut de luxe red with a fetching cockerel and feather duster label. Intrigued?

NEW ZEALAND

9 **The Ned Pinot Noir 2012**   £12.49
Whopping Waihopai (Marlborough) red burgeons with summer-pudding fruits kept in trim by a kind of leafy, almost austere structure that fascinates all along the great length of grippy, lush flavour.

9 **Martinborough Vineyard Pinot Noir 2010** £30.00
This is the original, definitive Kiwi Pinot Noir, and I swear it's still my favourite, but the price is daunting; gorgeous ripe toffee lick edges the sweetly, mintily plump summer-pud fruit, but for all that, it's poised, restrained, elegant and graceful; 14% alcohol.

S. AFRICA

8 **Parcel Series Merlot 2012**   £7.99
Simple midweight part-oaked cherry-ripe party red does have a healthy weight and balance; 14% alcohol.

SPAIN

8 **Rioja Crianza Eguia 2007**   £8.99
Reassuring plump, blackcurrant, pure Tempranillo with vanilla-coconut oak in dignified late middle age.

9 **La Garnacha Salvaje del Moncayo 2011**   £9.99
Concentrated but vivid and juicy young varietal from northern Spain has crafty oak enrichment and gently gripping tannin. Exceptional for its freshness and vigour.

RED WINES

SPAIN

🍷 10 **Rioja Reserva Viña Ardanza 2004** £22.00
Among the dozens of Riojas at Majestic, this is my
number one, even at the price. Limpid ruby colour
is going discreetly orange at the rim and the perfume
includes orange zest as well as roast Spanish chestnut,
lush cassis and fleeting vanilla; for weight and balance it
is simply perfect.

🍷 8 **Clos du Bois Pinot Noir 2011** £12.49
Famous old Californian brand still delivers the distinctive
ripe-and-healthy, lush-but-grippy style of the state's
Pinots.

USA

🍷 10 **Clos du Bois Sonoma Reserve Merlot
2009** £18.99
Now here's a turn-up. A perfectly executed sunshine red
from California's least-fashionable grape; lavishly but
immaculately oaked and wildly lively and pure, with
14.5% alcohol. Why pay £1,000 for Pétrus when you
can have this for whatever price Majestic will be charging
on the day?

PINK WINES

9 **Yali Winemaker's Selection Merlot Rosé**
2012   £7.49
Strawberry pink in colour, nose and flavour, this fun, fresh
Colchagua wine is what rosé should be: an uncomplicated,
affordable pleasure; 11.5% alcohol.

8 **Domaine La Chautarde Rosé 2012**   £8.99
Pale-copper, dry, brisk, brambly-watermelon light
Provence pink for salads and seafood.

8 **Château Pigoudet La Chapelle Rosé 2012**   £9.99
Pale petal-pink Provence wine has positive crisp fruit
flavours; unusually focused, natural and freshly dry.

8 **AIX Rosé 2012 magnum**   £19.99
I admit that the magnum (1.5-litre) bottle is the principal
lure, but this Provence party piece with its delicate shell-
pink colour and fresh strawberry-redcurrant fruit has
other charms too.

8 **Poggio Argentiera Rosato 2012**   £9.99
Gaudy fun package for a soft, friendly, but crisp-finishing
fresh pink from Tuscany.

WHITE WINES

Majestic

ARGENTINA

8 Septimo Dia Chardonnay 2011 £9.99
Almost-buttery new-oaked confection is nevertheless true to the apple-peach and stone-fruit Chardonnay style; dry, minerally, wholesome.

AUSTRALIA

8 Paulett's Riesling 2011 £13.74
Pronounced citrus aroma lures you into this plush green-fruit, mineral and limey Clare Valley food wine; 11% alcohol.

8 Heggies Chardonnay 2011 £18.74
Ignore the tired, superannuated label, and thrill to the great wafts of peaches-and-cream pure Chardonnay pong, realised convincingly in the lush oaked freshness of the fruit.

8 Shadowfax Chardonnay 2010 £25.00
Left over from last year, when I sniffed at its Tolkienese nomenclature, this Beaune-style beauty is galloping along nicely; lush, mineral and mellowing.

CHILE

8 Santa Ema Sauvignon Blanc Reserva 2012 £8.74
Gooseberries, asparagus, broad beans, the lot in this allotment basket with crafty sweet, but lemon-tipped finish. Artful, appealing, safe, but not boring.

8 Yali Reserva Gewürztraminer 2012 £8.74
Big colour, recognisable lychee nose, plump-but-balanced exotic fruits; compares well in style and value to the Alsace model.

WHITE WINES

8 Leyda Chardonnay 2012   £10.99
Crafty coconutty 'single vineyard' rich sweet-apple dry
white gives a nod to Mâcon in its sunny mineral style.
I was completely taken in; 14% alcohol.

8 Terroir Hunter Riesling 2011   £11.99
From venerable Undurraga estate, a lemony and likeable
dry Riesling of the steely-but-aromatic kind (not the
German kind); lively and long.

8 Lacheteau Reserve Sauvignon Blanc 2012   £6.99
Tangy just shy of sharp, this is a lemon-grass party wine
of attention-grabbing zestiness. An anonymous 'Vin de
France' made in the Loire.

9 Picpoul de Pinet Villemarin 2012   £7.99
I am predisposed to liking Picpoul, and even more so in
the case of this well-made sea-fresh refresher with its tide
of glittering green fruitiness. Best of the year.

**10 Bourgogne Chardonnay Les Chenaudières
2012**   £8.99
This is the fun of it all – you just don't know where the
really great wines are going to turn up. Here's one: a
simple Mâconnais from the redoubtable Cave de Lugny
with an appositely macaroon savour alongside the ripe
apple-pie fruit and lemon soufflé lift. Sheer joy at a very
sensible price (at least by burgundy standards).

**8 Domaine du Pré Baron Sauvignon de
Touraine 2012**   £8.99
Humble provenance doesn't diminish the appeal of this
full-flavoured briny-grassy Loire refresher.

WHITE WINES

8 Valençay Le Clos du Château 2012   **£8.99**
Valençay's better known for its château (successively owned by Scots banker John Law and slimy statesman Talleyrand) than for its Sauvignon Blanc, but this one's a cracker: lashings of racy fruit and a crafty lick of richness.

8 Château de Cléry Muscadet de Sèvre et Maine Sur Lie 2012   **£9.99**
So many superb Muscadets from the nightmare vintage of 2012! This one has plenty of seaside zing in the crisp green fruit, and a convincing lemon twist at the finish.

9 Vouvray Domaine des Aubuisières 2012   **£9.99**
Chenin Blanc in the 'moelleux' (à la marrowbone jelly) style with lovely herbaceous honey notes is crisply balanced with a lemon acidity, coming out just off-dry, and infinitely delicious.

9 Pouilly-Fumé Les Cascadelles 2012   **£11.99**
Forceful, river-fresh, banks-of-the-Loire classic Sauvignon has a sneakily rich, ripe savour; flinty, fresh and stimulating.

8 Chablis Domaine Servin 2011   **£12.99**
Deeply coloured grown-up Chablis is properly flinty but rich and ripe too; beguiling.

8 Pinot Gris Réserve Domaine Zind Humbrecht 2011   **£14.99**
Rich colour and an intoxicating whiff of diesel amid the smokiness of this epic, unctuous but archly balanced Alsace classic; a friend to superior canapés and smoked fish; 14.5% alcohol.

WHITE WINES

FRANCE

 **8 Meursault Vieilles Vignes Le Meurger
2010** £24.00
Good, rich, but stony fresh and pure lavish burgundy of
the character you expect from this appellation and at this
price; safe to invest.

8 Falabella Blanco 2012 £9.99
From Terre di Chieti in Abruzzo, a well-coloured orchard-
fruit refresher with a nice nettly zip.

8 Fremondo Greco 2012 £9.99
From Sannio, north of Naples in the Campania, a
spearmint/honeysuckle-scented dry wine with limey zest
and racy freshness; neat creamy-pasta partner.

ITALY

8 Vermentino Poggio Argentiera 2012 £9.99
From Maremma (Tuscany), an appealingly floral dry
white with intriguing white-orchard-fruit notes, nutty
richness and delicate balance.

8 Masianico 2012 £12.49
Masi, a grand old family winery in the Veneto, makes
this peachy dry white from three parts Pinot Grigio to
one of Verduzzo grapes, sun-dried to concentrate them;
the effect is a lush, tropical-fruity but fresh and enticing
special-occasion wine, at a price.

N. ZEALAND

8 The King's Thorn Pinot Gris 2012 £12.49
Exotic, smoky, intense-but-dry – very dry – ripely aromatic
wine in the Alsace style (apart from the dryness); good
match for snails, smoked fish and charcuterie.

WHITE WINES

N. ZEALAND

🍷 8 **Main Divide Riesling 2011** £13.74
Aromatic rich off-dry aperitif wine with a Kiwi brightness all its own.

S. AFRICA

🍷 8 **Raats Granite Blocks Chenin Blanc 2012** £9.99
Dry nicely abrading but generously fruity roast-chicken wine; who wouldn't like a wine called Raats?

🍷 9 **Vega de la Reina Verdejo 2012** £8.99
Sweet blossomy nose on this fine Rueda wine leads to a lush meeting of ripe autumn fruit with fresh, crisp acidity; the Verdejo grape (not connected to the Verdelho of Madeira) is the Spanish variety to watch.

🍷 9 **Rias Baixas Caixas Albariño 2011** £9.99
I've been casting around for a good Albariño and here it is, though from 2011, not the current 2012; big, big white fruits in this groovily presented Martin Codax production, with wild seashore breeziness and long lushness.

SPAIN

🍷 8 **Viñas del Vero Gewürztraminer 2012** £9.99
Surprisingly dry and restrained Somontano aperitif with unmistakable lychee, spice and appetising fruits, but not in the gloopy Alsace style at all.

🍷 8 **Rias Baixas Deusa Nai Albariño 2011** £12.99
From Rioja bodega Marqués de Cáceres, a fine, sunny-ripe diversion to the wilder Atlantic shore with this lavish honeysuckle-scented daisy-fresh and intensely ripe dry food wine.

SPARKLING WINES

8 Bouvet Ladubay Saumur Brut £11.99
Busy Loire fizz with 'honeysuckle, acacia and bruised apples on the palate', says maker. Fair comment. Lively, likeable, undervalued sparkler owned by Taittinger Champagne.

9 Heidsieck Monopole Gold Top 2007 £30.00
Lavish colour and correspondingly full, ripe, brioche-perfumed, gorgeous mellow vintage champagne with bottle age; has been discounted to £20, which is a top bargain.

8 Prosecco Zonin Brut £10.99
Not as brut as you might expect; there's a residual sweetness, but not so much that it's an affront; decent big-brand freshly persistent fizzer with 11% alcohol.

8 Pelorus Brut £21.99
Cloudy Bay's celebrated Chardonnay sparkler is long, bready and uplifting, but needs a discount to compete with good champagne for value.

FRANCE

ITALY

N. ZEALAND

Marks & Spencer

There are 75 wines from Marks & Spencer recommended in the following pages. That's a good many more than in any previous edition, and a reliable indicator, I believe, of the continued progress M&S is making towards first place among all the mass retailers as a purveyor of choice, quality and value in wine.

Highlights include a lot of good-value reds from France, Italy and Spain at below £8 or so. And there is a better choice of Australian wines here – at all price levels – than anywhere else. But there are great wines right across both the Old and New Worlds, and of course all unique to M&S, which continues to adhere loyally to its own-brand culture.

A novelty this year – at least to me – is the packaging of quite a few of the wines in alternative sizes. There are handy 25 or 50cl bottles and a few in 1.5-litre 'pouches', the new environmentally friendly collapsing bags-without-boxes that are a recent innovation.

Don't expect to find all the wines mentioned here in every M&S branch. Some will be in the biggest stores only, although even larger outlets in my experience can have a rather limited range. The widest selection is to be found online at M&S Direct, where everything is offered in six-bottle cases for home delivery.

Don't hold me to it, but it seems to me that M&S have a more-or-less permanent 25 per cent off all the wines listed online. To qualify you simply need to order two six-bottle cases. Bear this in mind when studying the already very fair prices on the pages that follow.

RED WINES

8 **Hunter Valley Shiraz 2011**   £9.99
Muscular, trim variation on the eternal oaked Oz Shiraz
theme has spice and definition; made by Tyrrell's.

8 **Mule Sangiovese 2010**   £13.99
McLaren Vale red from the grape of Chianti tastes
otherwise, a big pillowy plush black-fruit smoothie with
a nicely contrived edge; 14% alcohol.

8 **Tractor Tube Society Clare Valley Malbec
2011**   £13.99
Sun-baked leather-and-spice Malbec expensively aged in
new oak (not in old tractor tyres) renders a deep flavour
I'd like to imagine finding in Cahors; 14% alcohol.

8 **Duck Dam Heathcote Shiraz 2010**   £14.99
The names get madder and madder, but I did like this
roasty, near-burnt, plumptious creamy lush dark spice-
bomb (14% alcohol). Dish it up with, er, roast duck.

8 **Château Tanunda Mattiske Road Shiraz
2011**   £16.99
Toasty-oaked Barossa winter warmer is deep purple with
deep, dark, spicy fruit and 14% alcohol; deeply delicious
for those with deep pockets.

9 **Red Claw Mornington Peninsula Pinot
Noir 2011**   £17.99
Beautifully coloured limpid Pinot leads on to a lovely
big ripe farmyard cherry-tree serious-burgundy style of
ineffable (as you can tell) wonder; roast-fowl red.

RED WINES

Marks & Spencer

CHILE

8 Ulmen Carmenère 2012　　　　　　　£5.99
Sweet-tooth blackberry red is neatly trimmed for a dry finish; 14% alcohol.

8 Soleado Merlot 2012　　　　　　　£6.49
Defined pure-fruit intense but nicely weighted ripe red by Cono Sur winery.

FRANCE

7 Vin de Pays de l'Ardèche Gamay 2012　　£4.99
Maybe it's me, but this perennial cheapie from the Beaujolais grape is not what it used to be; it's light, with raspberry fruit, but not in the Beaujolais style at all. Do try it though, cool.

8 Côtes du Rhône Villages 2011　　　　£7.99
Pure, peppery typical CdR without oak but plenty of warm ripeness from very busy Celliers des Dauphins; 14% alcohol.

8 Domaine Mandeville Shiraz 2012　　　£7.99
They say Syrah, not Shiraz, in the Languedoc where this comes from, but that besides, it's an honest, concentrated, grippy-spicy Med red, in a super-light PET bottle.

8 Old Vines Grenache Noir 2011　　　　£8.99
Strong dark Languedoc red is just short of baked and has a likeable fruit-cakey savour; 14% alcohol.

8 Bourgogne Pinot Noir 2010　　　　　£9.99
I'm glad I persisted when tasting this, getting past the odd spearmint nose and into the lovely colour and silky, tightly defined and elegant summer soft fruit. Lush.

RED WINES

FRANCE

🍷 9 **Domaine de Fontsèque Corbières 2010** £9.99
Corbières is cursed with a name for cheapness and coarseness, but this deep-purple, intense, blackberry-pie-with-cream Mediterranean thriller is a very different animal. Love the coffee and dark chocolate notes and grabby dry finish.

🍷 8 **L'Etoile Romanin 2010** £14.99
Provence blend of Syrah, Grenache, Mourvèdre and Cabernet is dramatically dense, lavishly rich (yet unoaked) and natural-tasting. Gets to you.

🍷 9 **Châteauneuf-du-Pape Les Closiers 2009** £19.00
In spite of the price, I really recommend it: a complex, nuanced, basket-of-spicy-dark-fruits classic that's properly mellowed out and satisfying.

ITALY

🍷 9 **Popolino Rosso 2012** £4.99
Perky, juicy party red from Sicily makes a nice match for pasta and pizza. Remarkable value, and charmingly named.

🍷 8 **Merlot delle Venezia 2012** £5.49
Endearingly sweet cherry nose on this Beaujolais-like contrivance leads into balanced fresh red-berry fruit; it is 'naturally low in alcohol' at 10.5%. Try it chilled.

🍷 9 **Reggiano Rosso 2012** £5.99
This is Lambrusco: a dark, juicy blackcurrant red from Lambrusco grapes grown in Emilia-Romagna. It's a still wine, and like the better-known fizzy version should be chilled. Delicious!

RED WINES

8 Toscano Rosso 2012   £5.99
Convincing Chianti-style red brims with healthy fruit.

9 Aglianico Benevento 2012   £6.49
Dense deep-purple colour and spicily ripe dark flavours in
this agreeably abrading Campania wine. Distinctive and
wholesome.

8 Dolcetto d'Asti 2012   £6.99
By Piedmont giant Araldica, this has a cheerfully lurid
deep magenta colour and brambly puckering bright fruit;
sticky pastas, saucy meats.

8 Frappato Santa Tresa 2012   £7.99
Just the red side of rosé, it has trim, balanced red-berry
fruit (Frappato's the grape) and delicate weight.

9 Perricone Caruso e Minini 2011   £7.99
Colour borders on black in this roasted-fruit Sicilian
with velvety black-fruit pungency and a lip-smacking dry
finish; tastes expensive; 14% alcohol.

8 Pinot Nero IGT Dolomiti 2012   £8.99
Earthy Pinot Noir from the Dolomites is cherry-ripe and
plump with firm tannins; distinctly fruity and fun for
serving cool.

7 Chianti Villa Cerna 2012   £9.99
This decent wine comes in a fiasco, a raffia flask from
the far past, so it costs more than it would otherwise.
Innocent fun.

ITALY

Marks & Spencer

RED WINES

ITALY

🍷 8 **Masi Bardolino 2011** £10.99
Untypically robust and intensely coloured, this has heaps of bright cherry fruit and grip, and a fine elegant ripeness. As good a Bardolino as I can recall. Online only.

🍷 10 **Morellino di Scansano 2009** £15.99
It's just like the monster plummy-minty reds of Montalcino, very dark (and this case going gently tawny with age) with silky richness, a bitter-chocolate centre and lavish long black-fruit flavours. De luxe super-Chianti with 14% alcohol.

🍷 9 **Renato Ratti Marcenasco Barolo 2009** £27.00
I am accustomed to disappointment in Barolo, but this is spot on. Colour is going oloroso brown and it has a gorgeous gamey ripeness at the core of the slinky pure fruit; 14% alcohol.

NEW ZEALAND

🍷 9 **Flaxbourne Merlot 2011** £9.99
Adorable poised plump black-cherry red from Yealands Estate at Gisborne is light in colour but substantial in sheer fruit ripeness. Online only.

🍷 9 **Clocktower Pinot Noir 2010** £13.99
Kiwi Pinot is getting fashionable; this slinky, pure-tasting number by Wither Hills gives a clue. It's gorgeous, dahling.

🍷 8 **Earth's End Pinot Noir 2011** £15.99
I was completely taken in by this sweetly poised pale and deeply interesting Pinot; 14% alcohol.

RED WINES

SOUTH AFRICA

9 Cape Red 2012 £4.99
Cheap mix of Cinsault and Ruby Cabernet has Mediterranean briary-spicy charm; healthy, juicy fruit. Top value.

7 Crow's Fountain Shiraz Merlot Pinotage 2011 £5.99
If you like sweet dark fruit in your wine, try this savoury, tarry Stellenbosch economy blend; 14.5% alcohol.

SPAIN

8 Bodegas Murviedro GSM 2012 £6.99
Garnacha, Monastrell and Syrah in equal parts make up this fresh berry-bright spicy picnic red from Valencia.

8 Blau Montsant 2011 £9.99
Esoteric new-oak-aged near-black spicy sausage red from DO next to Priorat and similar in style; 14.5% alcohol. Online only.

8 Escondite Perfecto Mencia Bierzo 2010 £9.99
Dark, lip-puckering, potent (14% alcohol) food wine from ace producer Martin Codax; roasted black fruit with creamy richness.

10 Rioja Campo Aldea Graciano 2008 £12.99
You're looking for the perfect Rioja? Buy this. It's not typical, being pure Graciano grape (none of the usually statutory Tempranillo and Garnacha), but it's nevertheless 100% Rioja (and 14% alcohol) and transcendingly juicy, rich and lingering.

PINK WINES

FRANCE

8 **Gold Label Rosé 2012** £7.99
Assertive soft-summer-fruit dry wine with plenty of flavour is pure Syrah from the Languedoc. Honest fare.

8 **Fleur d'Amélie Rosé 2012** £9.99
From Bordeaux Château de Sours, well known for rosé, a deep-pink, mainly Merlot, crunchy crisp cherry-strawberry fruit basket of real freshness and zing.

HUNGARY

7 **Hungarian Pinot Grigio Rosé 2012** £6.99
Sounds awful, has a pale, onion-skin colour, but is cleanly, pinkly fresh with a little PG smokiness; 11% alcohol.

ITALY

8 **Monferrato Chiaretto Rosé 2012** £6.49
Bright, florally scented dry wine from (mostly) Barbera grapes has a chirpy, hedgerow-in-bloom fruitiness that works.

SPAIN

8 **Las Falleras Rosé 2012** £4.99
From Utiel-Requena, a candy-floss pink that's cheap and not oversweet.

WHITE WINES

AUSTRALIA

🍷 8 **Hunter Valley Chardonnay 2012** £9.99
Unoaked, luscious, but tangy Tyrrell wine is just right for fruit and balance.

🍷 8 **Mule Viognier 2011** £13.99
Old-fashioned toffee-and-apricots revival of once-trendy variety Viognier is expensively oaked, nicely poised and worthy of a shellfish occasion.

AUSTRIA

🍷 8 **Rabl Grüner Veltliner 2012** £7.99
Herbaceous dry white of real interest to match Eastern dishes.

CHILE

🍷 8 **Viña Ulmo Sauvignon Blanc 2012** £6.49
Rather profound green-grass fruit grows on you from this easy-drinking refresher by Luis Felipe Edwards.

🍷 9 **PX-Elqui 2011** £6.99
From Pedro Ximenez, the sweetening grape in sherry, this is a fresh, dry white with generous melon-peach fruit and a fine balance. Love it.

🍷 8 **Paradiso Sauvignon Blanc 2012** £7.99
Nettles on the nose and a lick of sweetness at the back of the seagrass fruit in this shamelessly commercial contrivance from Luis Felipe Edwards.

ENGLAND

🍷 7 **Lamberhurst Estate Bacchus Reserve 2012** £11.99
Sherbetty twang finishes off this decent dry Kentish aperitif wine; unrealistic price, though.

WHITE WINES

**7 Picpoul de Pinet Les Vignerons de
Florensac 2012** £8.49
Easy-drinking fashionable dry Mediterranean white has
lots of orchard fruit and less greenness of acidity than
some.

8 White Burgundy 2011 £8.99
Safe healthy nutty-ripe unoaked Chardonnay; I have not
tasted the 2012.

8 Sauvignon Blanc de St Bris 2011 £9.49
St Bris neighbours Chablis, but makes its dry white wines
from Sauvignon, not Chardonnay. This one is mineral,
racy and gently green; distinctive.

8 Fleur d'Amélie Blanc 2012 £9.99
Dry traditional Sauvignon-Semillon blend from rated
Bordeaux Château de Sours is restrained, elegant, partly
oaked and a bit de luxe.

9 Chablis 2010 £10.99
Well-coloured, leesy, luxuriant proper Chablis of true
character from respectable La Chablisienne co-operative.
Seriously good.

8 Crozes-Hermitage Blanc 2011 £12.99
From a northern Rhône outpost much better known for
reds, this pure Marsanne is plushly vegetal, dry but ripe
and rather expensive.

FRANCE

WHITE WINES

FRANCE

🍷 8 **Châteauneuf-du-Pape Les Closiers Blanc 2011** £17.99
If you're minded to drink white Châteauneuf, try this one. It's extravagant but not oak-aged, retaining the lush freshness of its layered, rich, complex white fruits.

GERMANY

🍷 9 **Palatia Pinot Grigio 2012** £8.49
Perennially admirable Rhine PG is limey, smoky, stonily fresh and contemplative. Always a step ahead of the Italians.

ITALY

🍷 7 **Toscana Bianco 2012** £5.99
Soft, flowery and fresh Vermentino-Chardonnay concoction is dry, easy and, I noted, evocative of greengage.

🍷 8 **Giardini Veneto Tai Pinot Grigio 2012** £6.49
Prickly fresh, tangy-nutty, Sauvignon-style confection made partly with semi-fermented juice to keep alcohol low (9.5%) is a legitimate product.

🍷 8 **Vermentino di Sardegna 2012** £7.49
I am a sucker for Sardinian wines; this has sunny colour, almond-blossom whiff and floral dry fruit with a white-nut creaminess.

🍷 8 **Zibibbo Cantine Fina 2012** £7.49
Made in Sicily by a man called Chioccioli, this scores for nomenclature; it's pale, vibrantly zingy and crisp, and the hint of honey reveals the Zibibbo grape as a Muscat family member.

WHITE WINES

ITALY

7 Ascheri Langhe Arneis 2012   £12.99
Dry but luxuriant Piedmont show-off white with layered, almondy aroma and corresponding flavours.

NEW ZEALAND

10 Emerald Cove Sauvignon Blanc 2012   £9.99
A standout Sauvignon from Lawson's Dry Hills winery in Marlborough has glittering, briny green fruit by the bucketful. Perfection. The price, for this quality, clinches it as a maximum scorer.

8 Seifried Estate Nelson Pinot Grigio 2012   £9.99
Smoky, startlingly zippy spin on the PG phenomenon is assertively delicious, if you like this sort of thing.

9 Kaituna Hills Reserve Sauvignon Blanc 2012   £11.99
Utterly consistent M&S brand is again fabulous in this new vintage, bright with gooseberry aromas, lush with classic meadow-grass-at-dawn Kiwi Sauvignon fruit.

PORTUGAL

8 Tapada de Villar Vinho Verde 2012   £6.99
The fruit keeps up with the spritzy lemon twang in this unusually alluring 'green wine' with just 10.5% alcohol.

SOUTH AFRICA

8 Dolphin Bay Chardonnay 2012   £5.79
Budget wine has virtues of simplicity: apple-fresh and lively with a note of clove; 14% alcohol.

8 Crow's Fountain Chenin Blanc 2012   £7.99
Particularly dry and brisk variation on the virtuous Cape Chenin theme, this is a stimulating refresher with a trace of creamy richness.

WHITE WINES

SOUTH AFRICA

Y 8 **Journey's End Honeycomb Chardonnay**
2012 £9.99

The 'honeycomb' in the name is a misnomer. This is a cheerfully cabbagey Stellenbosch Chardy with apple-pie ripeness, long flavours and real crispness. Terrific.

Y 9 **Villiera Barrel Fermented Chenin Blanc**
2012 £11.49

Pure white peach and a butterscotch background to this sublimely balanced Stellenbosch de luxe dry lobster wine; the appeal is akin to that of white burgundy, but with added dimension; 14% alcohol.

SPAIN

Y 8 **Toque Virtuoso Sauvignon Blanc 2012** £6.99

Attractive greeny-gold Valencian is grassy with a lick of richness; a different twist on the Sauvignon theme.

SPARKLING WINES

FRANCE

8 Oudinot Champagne Brut £25.00
M&S's house champagne is pure Chardonnay and very
consistent, with generous brioche style, long, positive
fruit and heartening signs of bottle age.

ITALY

7 Prosecco Frizzante £7.49
Very gently fizzing, pale Veneto frother is in the dry style;
11% alcohol.

7 Prosecco Zardetto £11.99
A 'spumante' sparkler much fizzier than the above
'frizzante' with soft (just short of sweet) orchardy fruit;
11.5% alcohol.

N. ZEALAND

7 Mount Bluff Sparkling Sauvignon Blanc £11.99
Busy, persistent mousse in this refreshing carbonated
oddity from Marlborough; it does indeed taste a lot like
sparkling Sauvignon Blanc.

Morrisons

Only one in four of us know what we're doing when we buy a bottle of wine. So says a survey, conducted among 2,000 wine drinkers, for Morrisons, in 2013. It reveals that while most of us claim to know what we like, few have any idea how our preferences can be translated into what kind of wine we should choose.

This state of affairs has galvanised Morrisons, which has lately launched a new online wine operation under the name Morrisons Cellar, expanding dramatically on the store range. 'Recognising the uncertainty of wine shoppers,' they declare, 'Morrisons has launched a unique Taste Test tool asking three simple non-wine-related questions: how you take your coffee, if salt is added to your food and your preference for full-fat or no-added sugar in fizzy drinks.'

On the basis of the answers to three simple multiple choice questions, Morrisons reckon they can establish what style of wine the respondent will like. There are four categories: sweet, fresh, smooth and intense. Every one of the thousand-or-so wines Morrisons sell has been allocated a number that indicates the style, and its degree, thus 0 to 3 for sweet, 4 to 6 for fresh, 7 to 9 for smooth and 10 to 12 for intense.

I learned all about this at a special tasting of a large number of the wines, and I do congratulate Morrisons on their enterprise. I understand how hard it is to guess what any wine will taste like when all you have to go on is the colour and the label, so any guidance must surely be welcome.

For what it's worth, I scored 5 in the taste test, which puts my preference in the middle of the fresh range (4 to 6). In fact, most of the wines I preferred on a subjective basis were from other categories. I'm an awkward customer, I suppose.

A lot of the new wines are, for the moment, available only online. Where this is the case, I mention it in the following pages.

RED WINES

ARGENTINA

8 **La Consulta Reserve Malbec 2011** £9.99
I wrote 'moody' in my note on this deep-purple spicy and satisfying Andean meat-matcher.

CHILE

9 **Serie Riberas Syrah 2010** £12.19
Charmingly lush and poised vivid oaked special-occasion red by giant Concha y Toro; something like a northern Rhône style; 14.5% alcohol.

8 **Cono Sur 20 Barrels Pinot Noir 2010** £18.19
Dense cherry colour corresponds to the luxuriant fruit in this princely Pinot from dependable Cono Sur; there's rich oak, but the fruit comes out on top; 14% alcohol.

FRANCE

8 **Vaucluse Grenache Syrah** £3.99
Genuine dry non-vintage southern plonk has easy fruit and a distinct pomegranate perfume.

8 **Terroir du Midi Fitou 2011** £4.99
Tight but not tough middleweight Mediterranean food wine with brambly-spicy fruit and grip.

8 **Château Laubès 2009** £7.99
Deeply coloured convincing claret from a great vintage is ripe and ready. Online only.

10 **Lirac Ogier La Marlerie 2011** £8.99
Superb Rhône red has lavish, complex deep blackberry fruit with summery raspberry juiciness and a creamy richness, I guess from oak contact. It truly warms the cockles. It is 15% alcohol, but it wears its power lightly.

RED WINES

FRANCE

🍷 8 **Savigny-lès-Beaune 1er Cru Les Marconnets 2009**   £15.99
Authentic earthy-summery burgundy is a safe investment. Online only.

🍷 8 **Château de Malleret 2004**   £16.99
Roundly mature and silky Haut-Médoc is Merlot dominated but still convincingly vigorous; reasonable value. Online only.

ITALY

🍷 8 **Trezanti Rosso 2011**   £7.99
Sunny, silky and spicy oaked black-fruit Salento (Puglia) pasta-partner from Negroamaro grapes.

🍷 9 **Nostro Meglio Barbera d'Asti Superiore 2009**   £8.99
Slick, oak-matured, blueberry-briar, typically juicy Piedmont classic is instantly likeable; 14% alcohol.

SOUTH AFRICA

🍷 8 **Tiger Horse Old Vine Cinsault 2011**   £6.99
Pale-coloured but nicely gathered middleweight grippy hedgerow red has a fun toffee nose and a pinch of pepper at the finish; 14.5% alcohol.

🍷 8 **Warwick Old Bush Pinotage 2010**   £13.99
You get a nice hint of treacle in this dry, trim and yet portentously savoury and ripe example of South Africa's national grape. Try it, at Morrisons' suggestion, with shepherd's pie; 14.5% alcohol. Online only.

RED WINES

SPAIN

9 Three Houses GSM Spanish Red   **£4.49**
GSM stands for constituent grapes Grenache, Syrah and
Mourvèdre, all used to good effect in this purple, spicy-
sweet, briary and balanced cheapie from Valencia. Great
value and a good chilli match.

8 Bobal Valsan 1831 2011   **£6.99**
Raspberry-ripe and earthy style to this deep-purple,
briary and gripping paella-partner from Utiel-Requena
region. Online only.

8 Cuatro Pasos Bierzo 2010   **£9.99**
Vivid purple middleweight by Martin Codax with firm
tannin evokes blackberry pie with cream; 14% alcohol.
Online only.

9 Baron de Ley Rioja Gran Reserva 2001   **£13.99**
Dark and grippy classic from a fabled vintage has a
pungent, even spirity, perfume of cassis and vanilla;
it's still vigorous, as well as opulently rich, layered and
creamy.

WHITE WINES

ARGENTINA

🍷 8 **La Consulta Reserve Torrontes 2011**   £9.99
Distinctive sweetly ripe but structurally dry wine has a Muscat-grape aroma and lots of fresh, crisp, dessert-apple fruit with a spicy twist.

AUSTRALIA

🍷 10 **Wirra Wirra 12th Man Chardonnay 2011** £16.99
Brilliant, Meursault-like de luxe wine proves the rule that at the top of the order, the Aussies can make the world's best wines. This is plush, mineral, perfect wine, fairly priced, with modest 12.5% alcohol. Online only.

FRANCE

🍷 8 **Premières Côtes de Bordeaux**   £5.99
Discreetly luscious dessert wine has convincing trace of gold in the colour and a crafty balance of honeyed richness with citrus acidity; made by respectable Bordeaux merchant-grower Sichel.

🍷 8 **Première Vouvray 2011**   £6.49
Light, fleetingly honeyed, off-dry Loire white from Chenin Blanc grapes is leafy-delicate and, as the Morrisons buyer says, 'self-assured'.

🍷 8 **Badassière Picpoul de Pinet 2011**   £7.99
Plenty of ripe white fruit in this trendy summer slurper with sea-breeze freshness, from a winery founded by someone called Baron de Badass. Online only.

🍷 10 **Jean Biecher & Fils Pinot Gris Réserve
2011**   £7.99
A perfectly poised, dry smoky-spicy Alsace wine of ideal balance, this is deliciously exotic and layered in its herbaceous, orchardy flavours; the price is mystifyingly modest. Online only.

WHITE WINES

FRANCE

🍷 8 **Preiss Zimmer Gewürztraminer 2011**   £7.99
Strong lychee nose on this big, boldly spicy Alsace off-dry wine; it's above average thanks to its nicely controlled residual sugar.

🍷 8 **Château Saint-Amand 2007 37.5cl**   £10.19
Pure-gold ambrosial dessert wine from Sauternes is creamily rich and elegantly trim.

🍷 8 **Trimbach Muscat Réserve 2010**   £14.78
Rare Alsace wine from terrific Trimbach is very dry but very grapy, aromatic and exotic too. Online only.

GERMANY

🍷 9 **Paulinshof Riesling Kabinett 2011**   £15.56
Peachy delicate moselle has the faintest spritz and loveliest sweet-apple ripeness; a rare treat, with 10% alcohol. Online only.

ITALY

🍷 8 **Mandarossa Fiano 2011**   £9.99
Highly coloured Sicilian dry wine is assertive in its crunchy-apple freshness, but plump, long in flavour and satisfying too. Good creamy pasta-matcher. Online only.

NEW ZEALAND

🍷 8 **Yealands Black Label Pinot Gris 2010**   £12.99
Dry wine with a lick of smoky richness from Marlborough, with a nod to Alsace; a serious food wine (fishy stews and white meats). Online only.

🍷 8 **Spy Valley Envoy Riesling 2011**   £14.99
Intense sherbet-honey rich balancing act for aperitif drinking in the German auslese manner, with just 8.6% alcohol. Online only.

WHITE WINES

S. AFRICA

♆ 8 **Ken Forrester The FMC 2010** £23.99
Yellow, rich, but fresh and brisk, luxury dry Chenin Blanc of astounding quality and price. Rare treat with 14.5% alcohol. Online only.

♆ 9 **Torres Floralis Moscatel Oro 50cl** £7.99
In a shamelessly gaudy gilded bottle, this nectar is autumn gold in colour with matching mellow perfume suggesting everything from rose to lemon verbena; lush grapy flavour is honeyed but balanced; 15% alcohol.

♆ 8 **Viña Ludy Albariño 2011** £7.99
Seaside-fresh dry Galician mollusc-matcher incorporates a beguiling blanched-almond richness with the briny aroma and fruit. Zingy refresher.

SPAIN

♆ 9 **Arindo Rueda Veredjo 2011** £10.99
Floral nose is followed up by sumptuous but apple-crisp white fruit of palate-twanging zest; a top example of a fashionable style. Online only.

♆ 8 **Mara Martin Godello 2011** £10.99
Generously ripe and well-balanced dry white from Galicia is plump with orchard fruits, and yet wildly refreshing; lives up to the jazzy packaging. Online only.

Sainsbury's

'In the last financial year,' says Andy Phelps, drinks boss at Sainsbury's, 'our sub-£5 wines sales have declined, while sales of wines priced between £7 and £9.99 have increased by 11 per cent, and £10-and-over bottles have grown by 24 per cent.'

If Sainsbury's is a thermometer of the wine market, we can see where things are going. And at above £5, this retailer is certainly turning up the heat. The new 'Winemakers' Selection' range of own-label wines – which 'sits between House, our everyday value varietal range, and Taste the Difference, our premium range,' says Andy – is an interesting mid-price band with a lot of wines customers will warm to. Some of the wines are below £5, curiously enough, but most seem to be nailed at the £5.99 and £6.99 price points. More than a dozen of these wines, all new to me, feature in the following pages.

For the moment, however, it's the Taste the Difference wines that continue to impress me the most. They account for half the wines I have picked out from the vast overall Sainsbury's range this year, including four maximum scores.

Sainsbury's deserves credit for having introduced the concept of supermarket own-label wines, back in the 1970s, and for maintaining a consistency, if not a supremacy, in this field of endeavour ever since. If they hadn't had the idea in the first place, I fancy that the remarkable in-house ranges now to be found in all the major retailers might today be considerably less diverse, adventurous and keenly priced than they are. We would all be the losers for that. Hands up who would like to return to the days when the space on supermarket wine shelves was monopolised by Don Cortez, Hirondelle and Liebfraumilch.

RED WINES

ARGENTINA

🍷 8 **Taste the Difference Morador Malbec 2012 £7.99**
I liked the baked fruit in this leathery but not tough
barbecue red with the dark savour and considerable
poke (15% alcohol) that marks out the more interesting
Argentine Malbecs.

🍷 8 **Viñalba Cabernet Sauvignon Malbec Merlot**
2010 **£9.99**
Bordeaux-type blend from Mendoza comes out as
a sophisticated if saddle-tenderised plummy-raisiny
fruit bomb with 14.5% alcohol and a good grip of the
tastebuds.

AUSTRALIA

🍷 8 **DB Reserve Petite Sirah 2009** **£9.49**
Bright purple gripper has easy weight with a pungent
liquorice core and intriguing sweet-briar top notes.
Thought-provoking intense red from De Bortoli.

🍷 8 **Taste the Difference McLaren Vale**
Grenache 2010 **£10.49**
Sophisticated lushly oaked spicy dark heavyweight has
a leafy liveliness as well as intense fruit purity; 14.5%
alcohol.

CHILE

🍷 8 **Taste the Difference Chilean Merlot 2011** **£6.99**
Blood-red, straightforward morello-sweet, but correctly
dry-finishing, oak-smoothed friendly red from Errazuriz.

🍷 8 **Taste the Difference Chilean Pinot Noir**
2011 **£7.99**
Cushiony plump, cherry-raspberry, ripe but nicely dry,
typical Chilean Pinot from Santa Helena winery in
Casablanca Valley; 14% alcohol.

RED WINES

9 Longue-Dog Grenache Shiraz 2012 £5.49
Who can resist the stretched sausage-dog label? Few
of us, if the popularity of this Languedoc brand is any
indication. But the wine is genuine, cunningly ripe, soft
and juicy with a nice lift of acidity. Even the price is good.

8 SO Organic Shiraz Pays d'Oc 2012 £5.99
Pale crimson wine's aroma brings to mind a heap of new-
picked blackberries wrapped in the crushed leaves; well
anyway, a juicily appealing briary-spicy-fresh red wine.

8 Winemakers' Selection Merlot 2012 £5.99
Winningly fruity black-cherry sunshine red from the Gard
is neatly made, finishes wholesomely clean and crisp.

**8 Winemakers' Selection Costières de Nîmes
2011** £6.99
Typical deep-purple, warmly ripe and spicy example
of this distinctive Mediterranean appellation has juicy,
jingly briar appeal; 14% alcohol.

9 Winemakers' Selection Red Burgundy 2011 £7.69
Superbly well-knit and polished sweetly ripe Pinot Noir
by Antonin Rodet (so possibly Chalonnais), this is partly
aged in new oak to luscious effect. Good value.

8 Taste the Difference Languedoc Red 2012 £8.99
Deep-purple Mediterranean starchy-food red is darkly
spicy with sinewy briar fruit.

RED WINES

10 Château La Tulipe de la Garde 2010 £9.99
Merlot-dominated Bordeaux Supérieur is deep, blood red, a soupy modern claret of savoury ripeness, luxury oak smoothness and firm grip. From a famous vintage, it has 14.5% alcohol, and a delightful name.

9 Taste the Difference Pic St Loup 2011 £9.99
This obscure but sought-after Languedoc wine, named after a prominent mountain in the region, is catching on (the Co-op has also just introduced one). Immediately inviting blackberry-pie aroma and focused spicy dark Syrah-Grenache fruit, at a competitive price.

9 Taste the Difference Gigondas 2011 £13.49
Prestige southern Rhône appellation lives up to its name in this proper roasty and clinging spicy dark-chocolate-hearted slick oaked winter red with 14% alcohol, made by regional celebrity Gabriel Meffre. The price in this case is merited.

8 Saint Joseph Les Challey's Delas 2009 £14.99
St Joseph in the northern Rhône makes pure Syrah reds often of meaty robustness. This one is deep, dark, developed and gamey, with spice and grip; delicious and typical.

**8 Taste the Difference Châteauneuf du Pape
2011** £14.99
'Complex aromas of plums, truffles and spice', the label boasts of this splendid and satisfying Rhône classic from mega regional producer Skalli; it's already drinking well but will develop, and has a ripe 14.5% alcohol.

FRANCE

RED WINES

9 **Louis Max Mercurey 2010**   £15.99
Attractively labelled burgundy from unfashionable Mercurey quarter of the Chalonnais is an earthy, vivid and richly developed classic Pinot Noir of really enticing style. Classic Selection.

9 **Châteauneuf du Pape Clos de l'Oratoire 2011**   £18.99
This looks so attractive on the shelf in its grandly labelled bottle that I felt honoured to get a taste of it. Hugely intense (15% alcohol) and multi-faceted, it's definitely a bespoke Châteauneuf, made by a man called Didier Couturier, and all kidding aside, it's worth the premium price, even to drink now.

8 **Taste the Difference Marzemino Veneto 2012**   £5.99
I am warming to this weird wine; it's almost rosé pale and has sweetly ripe cherry fruit that somehow finishes dry, with a dusting of white pepper. Drink cool.

8 **Winemakers' Selection Montepulciano d'Abruzzo 2011**   £5.99
Cheerfully gaudy new heraldic label draws the eye to a very decent bouncing strawberry-juicy hedgerow fruit, finishing brisk with a citrus twang.

8 **Winemakers' Selection Nero d'Avola 2012**   £5.99
Proper pruny pong on this long, dark and eager pasta red from Sicily's most distinctive grape made by the island's giant Settesoli co-op.

FRANCE

ITALY

Sainsbury's

RED WINES

9 **Winemakers' Selection Chianti Riserva 2010** £6.99

Plummy, rich, proper mature Chianti, interestingly not oak-aged, with backbone and the proper cut-glass finish; low price for a riserva.

8 **Winemakers' Selection Tuscan Red 2011** £6.99

Snazzy label reveals a sort of Chianti understudy with perky dark-cherry fruit and plenty of gentle tannin grip; lightish but likeable.

9 **Taste the Difference Primitivo del Salento 2011** £7.49

Fruit-cake depths and dark savour in this dense, oaked, pruny southern red with tight and defined dark fruit. It's special.

7 **Taste the Difference Barbera d'Asti 2011** £7.99

Very light – but recognisably bouncy and juicy – warm-weather red to drink cool.

8 **Taste the Difference Aglianico del Vulture 2009** £9.99

Irresistibly named Basilicata wine has deep earthy ruby colour and roasted fruit; the ripeness is a little close to burnt, so not for the faint-hearted; 14% alcohol.

10 **Taste the Difference Barbaresco 2009** £9.99

To me, this is the ace in Sainsbury's considerable Italian flush. It's a handsomely presented wine from the famed Piedmont DOCG, with paleish but enticing colour, sweet ripeness of cherries and violets, even roses, on the nose and lush, long, elegantly poised summer red fruit; 14% alcohol. At a tenner, a great introduction to a fabled wine style.

ITALY

RED WINES

ITALY

🍷 **9** Taste the Difference Barolo 2009 £15.99

Pale, browning Piedmont classic with a perfume evoking something between sun-baked sour cherries and cold tea might not sound promising, but this is a brilliant wine just the same, made by rated producer Ascheri; it's a big one, with 14.5% alcohol and slinky, creamy, cakey fruit.

N. ZEALAND

🍷 **9** Taste the Difference Central Otago
Pinot Noir 2011 £10.99

Slick pure racingly refreshing summer-fruit Kiwi Pinot with an urgently inviting lushness plumped up by some judicious oak; 14% alcohol and serious fun to drink discreetly cool.

PORTUGAL

🍷 **8** Winemakers' Selection Portuguese Red £4.99

Brightly fruity clove and cinnamon deep-bramble typical Lucitanian juicy sardine red from local Baga grape plus port varieties; non-vintage.

SOUTH AFRICA

🍷 **10** Kanonkop Kadette 2011 £9.99

Delectably tarry blend of Pinotage with Cabernet and Merlot has minty lift, bitter chocolate, even Bordeaux-like cedar; it's gorgeous and deeply satisfying, from one of the Cape's great estates, and very reasonably priced; 14% alcohol.

🍷 **8** Taste the Difference Fairtrade Cabernet
Sauvignon 2011 £9.99

Hugely ripe, but not overdone, dense, liquorice-hearted slurpy blackcurrant-essence oaked smoothie for now or to keep ('wonderful bottle-ageing potential' is claimed, for once) from the granite slopes of the Green Mountain in Wellington; 14% alcohol.

RED WINES

SPAIN

8 Conquistador Rioja Joven 2012 £5.69
Silly name for a vigorously blackcurranty, unoaked, pure-fruit, darkly ripe (14% alcohol) roast-beef red you might fail to recognise as Rioja.

**9 Taste the Difference Viñedos Barrihuelo
Rioja Crianza 2008** £8.99
Colour is showing orange at the rim – and did I detect an orange-zest fringe to the plump berry-fruit and vanilla nose? Flavour corresponds faithfully and it tastes well above price. Also sold in teeny 20cl bottle at £2.25 – fun!

7 Taste the Difference Priorat 2009 £10.49
Deep earthy ruby colour, gamey pong and rich-but-tough fruit with 14.5% alcohol. I'd risk keeping it a while, but the back label advises consuming it 'within one year of purchase'. Are they kidding?

PINK WINES

7 Winemakers' Selection Côtes du Rhône
Rosé 2012 £5.99
Magenta colour, soft strawberry fruit with redeeming dry
tang, it's refreshing enough and mildly interesting.

7 Taste the Difference Côtes de Provence
Rosé 2012 £7.99
Pale shell pink, delicate pale fruit with suggestions of
strawberry and redcurrant; dry.

8 Les Caillottes Sancerre Rosé 2012 £10.99
Show-off wine from the famed Loire appellation is pure
Pinot Noir, and it shows very plainly: dignified onion-
skin colour, dry, elegant, cherry-raspberry Pinot style, a
very proper pink, at a price.

FRANCE

Sainsbury's

WHITE WINES

🍷 **8** **McGuigan Classic Semillon Blanc 2012** £7.99
Exotic banana-pineapple fruit-basket aromas lead into
long, lush, fresh and quite dry yellow flavours in a wine
you might not immediately guess comes from Australia.

🍷 **8** **Leasingham Magnus Riesling 2009** £9.49
Grapey, intense, but dry, limey and exotic Clare Valley
food wine has long, shimmering flavours.

🍷 **8** **Taste the Difference Hunter Valley Semillon
2006** £9.99
Petrolly old wine is fino-sherry-like in its weighted density
and loaded with tropical fruits trimmed up into a dry
finish. I love it.

🍷 **8** **Taste the Difference Wild Ferment
Chardonnay 2011** £9.99
I'm not wild about the use of non-domesticated yeasts
(GM does me anytime) but this Yering Station wine does
convince with its balance of stony-pure Chardy fruit with
the lush oak enhancement.

🍷 **9** **Taste the Difference Grüner Veltliner 2012** £7.49
Austrian wines are probably a tough sell, but this
aromatic, mineral-velvet dry white from the rated
Traisental region is an eye-opener. Lush, nuanced aperitif
or delicate-flavour food wine.

🍷 **7** **Valdivieso Winemaker Reserva Sauvignon
Blanc 2012** £6.99
For Sauvignon followers who crave a softer style, this
asparagussy contrivance might serve.

WHITE WINES

**8 Winemakers' Muscat de St Jean de
Minervois 37.5cl** £4.99
Supersweet vin doux naturel burgeons with Muscat
honeyed richness to make an ambrosial aperitif or blue-
cheese partner; 15% alcohol.

8 Les Jardiniers Loire Sauvignon Blanc 2012 £6.99
Simple, ripe, grassy-lemony refresher with 11.5% alcohol.

9 Taste the Difference Mâcon Villages 2012 £6.99
Positive crisp-apple southern Burgundy Chardonnay of
great character, this is leesy and lush, unoaked and in the
Mâconnais style through and through.

**9 Taste the Difference Muscadet Sèvre et
Maine Sur Lie 2012** £6.99
There is plenty of good Muscadet from the 2012 harvest.
This one has a cheery seaside perkiness, lots of tangy
white fruit and a forgivable shortage of wincing green
acidity. Very friendly.

8 Vouvray Couronne des Plantagenets 2012 £6.99
Sainsbury's have been listing this esoteric Loire wine for
decades and it's as delicious as ever. It's a soft, not sweet,
Chenin Blanc with a mellow hothouse fruit lushness,
lemon twang and modest 11.5% alcohol.

**8 Winemakers' Selection Côtes du Rhône
Blanc 2012** £6.99
You don't see much white CdR; this one, from six
different grapes, is an orderly teaming of peachy ripeness
with brassica crispness to make an alluring whole, quite
dry but definitely exotic.

WHITE WINES

8 Taste the Difference Bordeaux Sauvignon
Blanc 2012 **£8.99**
Refined, grassy, typically spare Bordeaux style (this one's
from Blaye) delivers a rush of long green fruit; good.

10 Taste the Difference Languedoc Blanc 2012 **£8.99**
A successful repeat of the superb 2011 vintage. This
delicious Mediterranean mélange has freshness and tang
as well as a basketful of white fruits, and nice little toffee
lick to boot.

8 Taste the Difference Chablis 2012 **£9.99**
True Chablis character here, with a suggestion of sweet
spearmint and oyster-shell mineral purity.

8 Taste the Difference Limoux Chardonnay
2011 **£10.99**
This one's out of the box, a yellow, positively burgundian-
style apple-crumble-with-cream dry de luxe wine from
the Pyrenees.

10 Taste the Difference Pouilly Fumé 2012 **£11.49**
As in previous years, this just pips the TTD Sancerre (the
two appellations more or less face each other across the
Loire). This sublime Sauvignon kicks off with aromas of
asparagus, gooseberries and crushed nettles, moves on to
luxuriant grassy-orchard white fruits, and closes with a
satisfying lemon-lime tang. It speaks of the running river
and the sun that blazes down on to it.

9 Taste the Difference Sancerre 2012 **£11.49**
Another brilliant vintage for this consistent favourite
from the Loire. Stone-pure Sauvignon with leesy lushness
and lingering nettly fruit. The price is worth paying.

WHITE WINES

FRANCE

🍷 **8** **Taste the Difference Pouilly Fuissé 2012** £13.99
Not to be confused with the Loire wine above, a gold-coloured Mâconnais (Burgundy) from Chardonnay grapes: long, peachy-and-crunchy-apple fruit with discreet oak plumping.

GERMANY

🍷 **9** **Dr L Riesling 2012** £7.49
There's the faintest spritz in this racy but by no means bone-dry moselle from the sainted Ernie Loosen, who seems to have a near monopoly of quality German wine sales into UK supermarkets. A lovely delicate wine at a fair price, with just 8.5% alcohol.

🍷 **8** **Leitz Rheingau Riesling Spätlese 2012** £12.99
Full, sunnily ripe new hock has the prickly vivacity of racy Riesling fruit and 10% alcohol. Classic Selection.

ITALY

🍷 **8** **Winemakers' Selection Sicilia** £4.79
Orchardy Catarratto-Grillo non-vintage blend is dry, fresh and tangy at the finish.

🍷 **7** **Winemakers' Selection Orvieto Classico
2012** £4.99
Nice to see an Orvieto (from the tourist-mobbed hilltown of that name in Umbria) after a long absence, even if it's this 'amabile' or softly off-dry one, with a nice almondy whiff.

🍷 **8** **Winemakers' Selection Gavi 2012** £6.49
Aromatic but brisk, leesy example of this enigmatic Piedmontese dry white scores for exotic ripe white fruits; 11.5% alcohol.

WHITE WINES

 **Winemakers' Selection Falanghina de
Beneventano 2012** £6.99

Good definition and lemon tang ornament the orchard
fruit in this interesting and refreshing Campania dry
white, made with 10% Chardonnay.

 **Taste the Difference Pecorino Terre di
Chieti 2012** £7.49

Pecorino from the Abruzzi first made it onto the
supermarket shelves at M&S. Now it's everywhere; this
one has typical high colour and straight, fresh, tangy fruit.

 Taste the Difference Greco di Tufo 2012 £10.49

Rather expensive dry white from a new DOCG for
Greco grapes in the Campania, it has a fetching label and
equally alluring plushness of orchard fruit with a zesty
citrus acidity; memorable wine.

**Taste the Difference Riverblock Sauvignon
Blanc 2012** £9.99

Gooseberries to the fore in this straight, near-austere
Waihopai, Marlborough, grassy-racy refresher.

**Villa Maria Private Bin Gewürztraminer
2011** £9.99

Uncomplicated, unmistakable lychee- and rose-scented
Gewürz has bright spicy-grapey fruit and a lick of
sweetness. Compares well with the Alsace original.

Cloudy Bay Sauvignon Blanc 2012 £20.99

Icon wine has a fine waft of gooseberry-asparagus, even
peapod, perfume, and an eager rush of irresistible Kiwi
lushness and twang. But I feel that this lovely wine now
stands out from the crowd in only one respect: the price.

WHITE WINES

7 Winemakers' Selection Portuguese Vinho Verde £4.59

Unexpected apple-pear aroma from this non-vintage spin on Portugal's 'green wine' leads on to sweetly contrived white fruit and a soda-like spritz; very cheap and just 9% alcohol.

8 Torre de Azevedo Vinho Verde 2012 £6.99

Citrus aroma, barely detectable spritz, very dry but with a nice lift of orchard white fruit, this is in the authentic style, lively and fresh; 11% alcohol.

9 Winemakers' Selection Moscatel de Valencia £4.59

Honey and candied fruit mark out this gorgeous stickie; it's a well-made wine from part-fermented Muscat stopped with spirit (15% alcohol), in good balance. A bargain for the right occasion – e.g. cake, blue cheeses or just a mid-morning sharpener.

9 Winemakers' Selection El Pozo Bueno Rueda 2012 £5.49

Zingy near-astringent seashore-fresh simple Verdejo from a rightly rated Spanish region is a bargain.

10 Taste the Difference Albariño Rias Baixas 2012 £7.99

Another great year for this pioneer among Rias Baixas wines, launched yonks ago by Sainsbury's; this is thrillingly lush and eager, bursting with grassiness and white fruit, and scores maximum thanks to the consistently fair price.

WHITE WINES

SPAIN

🍷 8 **Taste the Difference Viñedos Barrihuelo Rioja Blanco 2012** £8.49

Modern (not oxidised in old oak) fresh dry wine from Viura grapes has alluring peach-blossom aroma and vivid lush white fruit.

USA

🍷 8 **Winemakers' Selection Californian Sauvignon Blanc 2012** £5.99

Good-value sweetish unoaked shamelessly commercial Sauvignon makes a change from Kiwi, and has 10% Chardonnay for good measure.

SPARKLING WINE

FRANCE

🍷 9 **Sainsbury's Champagne Blanc de Noirs** £21.99

Consistent top-value, all-Pinot supermarket own-label champagne has digestive-bikky pong, reassuring intensity of mellow fruit, and an oft-reduced shelf price.

Tesco

Rumour has it that of every dozen bottles bought off the shelf or online by British shoppers, three come from Tesco. But it's the quality that counts, and in the minds of many of the wine enthusiasts I know, size can subtly undermine belief in quality. While everybody knows that Tesco sells more wine than anybody else, not everybody assumes that it's the quality of the range that drives the sales.

Tasting a huge number of wines from Tesco, as I have this year, I must declare that this giant of giants is still very much in the race. The fact that in 2013 Tesco has recorded its first fall in profits in living memory may have made headlines, but it's having no discernible effect on the choice, interest and value offered by the wines. I am much relieved.

However, there does seem to me a reductive air, of sorts, at Tesco. Some of my long-term favourite wines have been delisted. My perennial Italian favourite Squinzano (who could resist the name?) Monte Nobile Rosso, a maximum scorer last year, has disappeared. So has neighbouring Molise red Gran Conti. These are both branded wines, and I suspect they may have been sidelined to make way for the continued growth of the own-label 'Finest' range, which does have some seriously good Italian co-productions among its 100-plus individual wines.

At a large Tesco tasting this year, the book of notes helpfully revealed how many stores stock each of the wines on show. Tesco Cava Brut – best value fizz under a fiver anywhere – is stocked, for example, in 2,314 outlets. Yes, you read it right – 2,314 of them. There are that many Tescos up and down the country. It's more than the total number of places permitted to call themselves towns. That's how big Tesco is.

All the same, there's no guarantee that all the wines mentioned in this section will be available from the branch nearest you. So take a look at the website, which has a wider selection than any of the individual stores, and offers many wines you won't find in any of them. It's a very efficient service, based on six-bottle-case purchases.

Delivery is free on orders of £100 or more, though sometimes it's £50 and sometimes it's unconditionally free except for the minimum order of one six-bottle case. Order before noon on any working day and you'll get your wine on the next working day.

RED WINES

8 **Finest Heritage Coonawarra Cabernet 2009 £9.99**
A deep brown-ruby evolved-tasting monster with lovely weight and balance from the Katnook Estate.

9 **d'Arenberg The Footbolt Shiraz 2009** £11.50
Iconic South Australian varietal is a mahogany dark electric soup of dense, savoury, peppery delights that dance delicately on the tongue; miraculous wine with 14% alcohol; online only at £69 per six-bottle case.

9 **Tim Adams Clare Valley Shiraz 2009** £12.99
Plummy, plush and toothsome, poised spicy Sunday-roast red from the presiding genius of the Clare; fascinatingly pure and elegant, it wears its 14.5% alcohol lightly.

8 **Peter Lehman Mentor Cabernet Sauvignon
2008** £18.00
Seductive mature ripe-blackcurrant Cabernet style to this utterly opaque and dark oaked Barossa wine has ideal weight, pleasing abrasion and 14.5% alcohol. Online only at £108 for a six-bottle case.

8 **Finest Kulapelli Cabernet Sauvignon
Carmenère 2012** £8.99
The slinky ripeness of fruit that is such a likeable Chilean trait is very evident in this plummy-cassis blend; a perfect shepherd's pie partner, I'd say.

9 **Tesco Corbières** £4.59
So ripe it's almost pruny, but this pure-Carignan non-vintage Med red has authentic fruits-of-the-forest charm and a big dark spicy grip; marvellous, and look at the price.

AUSTRALIA

CHILE

FRANCE

FRANCE

10 Tesco Beaujolais 2011 £4.79
Perhaps it has run out, but this bouncing, juicy thirst-quencher from the legendary 2011 vintage has been brilliant and extraordinary value; I have not tasted the 2012.

9 Finest Côtes Catalanes Carignan 2012 £6.99
Pitchy-purple colour and rich, concentrated briary fruit in this dense, spicy Pyrenean red, only marginally pipped for a top spot by its Grenache counterpart, immediately below.

10 Finest Côtes Catalanes Grenache 2012 £6.99
It looks a bit soupy, but this dark and brambly Perpignan wine has a finely judged weight and balance as well as exotic spice and grip; this is among the most consistently delicious of the Tesco range and, mysteriously, the price is more than £1 lower than for last year's excellent vintage.

8 Finest Gigondas 2011 £12.99
Generous but not galumphing southern Rhône prestige red has spicy top notes and a sweetly ripe fundament; big, sturdy winter red with 14.5% alcohol.

8 Louis Jadot Beaune Rouge 2007 £15.00
Well-seasoned burgundy from a long-lost vintage is gamey, earthy and browning, showing lush deep summer Pinot fruits; in its prime and worth the price of £90 per six-bottle case, online only.

RED WINES

FRANCE

♈ 9 Château Pédesclaux 2009 £24.99
A grand cru classé Bordeaux from the momentous 2009 vintage, this is a sleek modern claret with silky richness, a chocolate nuance, cedar spice and the flavour of money; at this price it's a bargain compared to other 2009 classed growths lately released by Tesco: Château Lafite at £800, anyone?

ITALY

♈ 8 Tesco Valpolicella 2012 £4.99
Cherry-perfumed pale Verona chilling wine has a wholesome nutty sweetness, crisp finish and just 11% alcohol.

♈ 8 Finest Chianti Riserva 2009 £7.99
Rich coffee and plump cherry nose on this finely weighted proper oak-aged wine by ubiquitous Piccini.

♈ 9 Finest Teroldego Delle Dolomiti 2010 £7.99
This fascinating, brightly fruity, leafy-edged and minty black-fruit wine from the sub-alpine Trentino region has been a brave move by Tesco; do try this vintage, which has been around for a while and is rounding out nicely.

♈ 8 Piccini Memoro £9.29
Four-grape blend from four Italian regions in who knows how many vintages, this Tuscan-produced dark, savoury oaked blend by Piccini has a seductive toffee richness, 14% alcohol and, somehow, a true Italian character. Frequently discounted.

RED WINES

PORTUGAL

9 **Finest Douro 2011** £7.49

This is easily the best vintage to date of this silky, profound red from the port vineyards; 2011 has been universally 'declared' as a vintage for port thanks to an ideal harvest, and the benefit clearly extends to the table wines too.

SPAIN

7 **Simply Garnacha 2012** £4.59

Jammy hedgerow red from Campo de Borja region will make a robust partner for hot, spicy dishes, and as such has real merit.

PINK WINES

FRANCE

🍷 8 **Finest Domaine de Sours Rosé 2012** £7.99
Pale copper colour to this dignified Bordeaux pink
resounds with black-cherry fruit from mainly Merlot
blend; it has verve and freshness and does taste as pink
as it looks.

🍷 7 **Finest Grenache Rosé 2012** £7.99
Copper-coloured Languedoc has clean, dry-finishing
briar fruit but looks a shade expensive.

PORTUGAL

🍷 8 **Finest Touriga Nacional Rosé 2012** £7.99
Bright magenta dry rosé from the principal port grape has
plenty of woof and a sweet backtaste, all in trim balance;
good all-occasions food wine.

SPAIN

🍷 8 **Simply Garnacha Rosé 2012** £4.59
I'm drawn to cheap rosés because pricier ones are so
rarely worth it; this shocking-pink brambly dry al fresco
wine from famed Bodegas Borsao fits the bill.

🍷 8 **Finest Navarra Rosé 2012** £6.99
Bright cherry hue, strawberry-ripe but crunchily crisp dry
refresher from Navarra – a dependable region for pinks.

WHITE WINES

8 Finest Denman Vineyard Semillon 2012   £9.99
Fresh-pineapple style to this dry Hunter Valley rendering of the protean Semillon grape; this is a uniquely styled wine all adventurous drinkers should try at least once; 10% alcohol.

8 Finest Tingleup Riesling 2012   £9.99
Perennial dry, limey, substantial mineral Riesling from a family winery is a modest 11% alcohol and a major treat.

10 Tim Adams Clare Valley Semillon 2011   £11.49
Cool, creamy, nutty, tangy – they all come into play in this glorious mélange, mostly of fruit fermented in new oak barrels; fascinating luscious wine just this side of dry and with a modest 11.5% alcohol. Try it with lobster, white chocolate or blue cheese.

8 Finest Tapiwey Sauvignon Blanc 2012   £8.99
First thing you notice is the pungent struck-flint nose on this powerful Casablanca limey-tangy dry wine; Chile does Sauvignon its own way, and all to the good.

**8 Luis Felipe Edwards Gran Reserva
Sauvignon Blanc 2012**   £9.99
Big ripe tropical dry wine has asparagus and even a bit of butter on the nose, leading into plumpness of leesy Sauvignon fruit finishing very brisk; online by the six-bottle case only.

8 Errazuriz Max Reserva Chardonnay 2011 £12.50
'Casablanca white burgundy', I call this; it's lavishly rich with toffee-apple intensity, yet nicely balanced between melon-ripe peach lushness and a grapefruit-tangy freshness. Cheaper than its Burgundian counterparts too; online only.

WHITE WINES

8 Tesco Vouvray £5.99
Near-dry Loire Chenin Blanc with honey at the back of
the floral aromas and flavours; intriguing non-vintage
aperitif with 11.5% alcohol.

**9 Finest Château Palatio Muscadet Sur Lie
2012** £6.99
Brightly crisp and briny-fresh bone-dry Loire seafood
white from a vintage rescued from terrible weather
difficulties; a triumph.

10 Finest St Mont 2011 £6.99
I can't fault it, so I won't. Cracklingly fresh and lush
Pyrenean blend of Gros Manseng topped up with Petit
Courbu and Arrufiac, it's a pure-gold dry white of
thoroughly distinctive character and a big advance in
quality even on the delicious 2010 vintage.

8 Finest Touraine Sauvignon Blanc 2012 £6.99
Tangy citrus Loire generic by Ackerman (known for
good, breezy regional sparklers) is emphatic enough to
bear comparison to the Kiwi style.

9 Finest Picpoul de Pinet 2012 £7.49
Best of the supermarket Picpouls this year, an attractively
presented new vintage of the trendy Mediterranean
holiday dry white; great oyster partner.

**9 Vin de Pays de Gascogne Gros Manseng
Sauvignon Blanc 2012** £7.99
Behind the distinctive heraldic label, another shining
vintage for this clever Gascon blend of lush peachiness
with zingy freshness. Stands way out from the crowd.

WHITE WINES

8 Finest Chablis Grand Cuvée 2012 £8.99

Good colour and a proper sweet-apple Chardonnay bloom from this generously fruity and mineral wine by the clever people at Blason de Bourgogne.

8 Finest White Burgundy 2011 £8.99

This does the job: proper sweet-apple, crisp-finishing Chardonnay by dependable Blason de Bourgogne; fresh, in spite of relatively long ageing with some oak contact.

8 Finest Sancerre 2011 £11.49

Very pale with a clear Sauvignon twang and grassy-nettle glitter of fruit. Proper Sancerre not improperly priced.

8 Finest Meursault 2011 £19.99

A bouquet of 'milk, bread, hazelnut, toast, roasted almonds and honey', says Tesco, and I won't argue. Luscious ripe classic is already drinking well, so a safe bet, or buy to keep a few years and look forward to 'hues of lime and quince'.

7 Tesco Frascati 2012 £3.99

Can't resist including this because it costs under £4 – an endangered species; a clean, crisp, anodyne example of the café wine of Rome.

8 Simply Soave Classico 2012 £4.79

Eager, zesty nose on a softer-than-expected ripely orchardy Soave with a lick of blanched-almond richness; charming, and cheap.

WHITE WINES

ITALY

♆ 9 **Finest Gavi 2012** £7.99
Almost colourless, but most unusually perky and defined
example of this mysterious Piedmont dry white; it's lush
but keen and edgy, and will make a ritzy partner for
grilled fish and other delicate flavours.

♆ 8 **Finest Soave Classico Superiore 2011** £7.99
Lots of colour and a beckoning blanched-nut aroma lead
into plush white orchard fruit and a tangy citrus edge; the
whole package is very attractive.

N. ZEALAND

♆ 8 **Giesen Estate Sauvignon Blanc 2012** £9.69
Whack of asparagus on the nose with correspondingly
assertive fruit in this big ripe Marlborough wine with a
saucy lick of richness.

SPARKLING WINES

9 Finest Premier Cru Champagne Brut £19.99
The 'Premier Cru' bit means the grapes come from higher-
rated vineyards, mostly Chardonnay from the Côtes des
Blancs; nice gold colour, long fruit, artful balance; bottle
looks alarmingly akin to former Bollinger style.

8 André Carpentier Champagne Brut £24.00
Bread and lemon-fresh full-fruit champagne by Jacquart
is plainly good and becomes doubly attractive when it is
discounted in regular promotions – one to watch.

**9 Finest Vintage Champagne Grand Cru
2007** £24.99
Pure Chardonnay from top-rated ('grand cru') vineyards,
this is a de luxe, mellow, bready-nosed and richly
developed champagne by any standard. And by vintage
champagne standards, believe me, it's cheap at the price.

10 Tesco Cava Brut £4.99
You get plenty of bang for your buck in this amazingly
animated sparkler made by cava giant Codorniu; it has
a fine stream, not just of busy bubbles, but of arch, crisp
and fresh orchardy fruits; how they do it for the money, I
cannot fathom; 11.5% alcohol.

8 Tesco Cava Reserva £6.99
It's a sweeter, fruitier, longer-tasting version of the younger
wine above, very decently made but less bewilderingly
underpriced.

Waitrose

What am I supposed to do? Waitrose lined up about 250 wines in their big tasting this year and I had to try all of them. I dare not skip any, because the next one could be the wine of the year. It's more likely to happen at Waitrose than at any other supermarket. It was a long day, but it was worth it. There are 117 wines recommended in this section, and I make no apology for any of them. Even a handful of Waitrose's fortified wines feature here, because they were included on the day. No one else bothers much with port and sherry at the sort of tastings I go to. Which is a pity.

Waitrose is growing. The number of outlets has doubled in not much more than a decade, and it is a consequence of this that a retailer once associated only with a small section of the market – the summit of it – must broaden its appeal. Through the wine department, Waitrose is doing exactly that. A new inexpensive range of own-labels is gradually insinuating itself. Look out for wines such as Waitrose Soft and Juicy Chilean Red at £4.99. It's cheap, it's non-vintage, and it's brilliant.

There are more Waitrose own-label wines in this section than ever before, for the very good reason that there are more Waitrose own-label wines. A new force in the market, I'd say.

And as I have been protesting for years, wine prices at Waitrose are fully competitive with all the other

chains. They have been for as long as I can remember.
And Waitrose is not too posh to promote. There are
scores of wines offered on discounts, frequently of up
to a third, in changing offers each month. And Wine
Direct, Waitrose's online service, has occasionally taken
to offering 25 per cent off all the wines on the website –
more than a thousand of them – as long as you order at
least one six-bottle case. Please note that the Waitrose
service allows you any mix of bottles you like; you don't
have to buy by the case.

Some of the wines that follow are stocked only in
a handful of mega-branches in London, but all are
available via Wine Direct, as pointed out in the notes.

RED WINES

🍷 8 Santa Julia Malbec 2012 £7.49

The first Argentine brand to break back into the UK market after the Falklands awkwardness, this is a soft toasty and yielding variation on the Malbec theme.

🍷 8 Tilimuqui Fairtrade Cabernet Sauvignon/ Bonarda 2012 £7.99

Plenty of dark, chocolatey-smooth plummy fruit in this well-made food red from the La Riojana co-operative, the world's largest Fairtrade wine producer; it's organic, to boot.

🍷 9 Norton Winemaker's Reserve Malbec 2010 £11.99

Dependable roasted-fruit plush monster Malbec with a manly leathery whiff of the gaucho about it, if I might be permitted the clunky metaphor; 14.5% alcohol.

🍷 9 Catena Malbec 2010 £12.49

I'm still getting over the pointless label-redesign on Catena wines but this juicy, darkly blackcurranty, muscular-but-supple briary fruit bomb is as gorgeous as ever and entirely worth the outlay.

🍷 9 Clos de los Siete 2010 £14.99

Opulent successor to the lavish 2009, this mainly Malbec (plus other Bordeaux varieties) Mendoza monster (14.5% alcohol) is chocolate-rich with berry fruits and creamy vanilla yet in fine balance; made by Bordeaux maestro Michel Rolland. Wine Direct.

RED WINES

AUSTRALIA

🍷 **8** **Waitrose Australian Shiraz 2011** £6.99
This is a right mouthful; ripe but not cooked spice-and-bramble juice explosion for a reasonable price.

🍷 **9** **Waitrose Reserve Shiraz 2011** £9.99
From St Hallett in the Barossa, a blood-red, beefy, satisfying roasty-spicy meat-matching red that's at once cushiony and comforting, and poised and defined; 14% alcohol.

🍷 **8** **Stonier Pinot Noir 2010** £13.99
Aussie Pinot gets left in the shade by the Kiwi competition, but here's a lovely Mornington Peninsula (Victoria) contender of real charm; pale, high-toned, pure-cherry-raspberry fresh-fruit flavours; exciting stuff, at a price.

CHILE

🍷 **10** **Waitrose Soft and Juicy Chilean Red** £4.99
The best of the new basic wine range, genuine sunshine wine from Merlot and Cabernet Sauvignon, elegantly balanced, easy weight but comfortably concentrated, satisfying and clean-finishing.

🍷 **9** **Luis Felipe Edwards Carmenère-Shiraz 2012** £5.99
Crimson colour, darkly juicy and roasty-spicy unoaked blend delivers a lot of fruit at the modest price. Luis Felipe Edwards crops up with reassuring frequency at all price levels.

🍷 **8** **Gato Negro Cabernet Sauvignon 2012** £6.99
Pure rounded cassis fruit with dark intensity and satisfying length of flavour in this artful food red; it has been 'aged in stainless steel tanks with toasted oak for three months', it says here.

RED WINES

CHILE

9 Miguel Torres Las Mulas Organic Cabernet Sauvignon 2012 £8.99
Pure, sleek Cabernet in the generous Chilean tradition is luxed up with six months in new oak casks (an expensive commodity) to impressive effect; intense, darkly ripe bargain.

ENGLAND

8 Wickham Special Reserve Red 2009 £13.99
Nose and fruit seem dominated by Pinot Noir, which comprises only 20% of the blend; a decent defined-fruit, cleanly balanced red for patriots, at a price. Wine Direct.

FRANCE

10 Cuvée Chasseur 2012 £4.99
Crafty Carcassonne blend of perpetual wonder is juicy and briary, with a note of regional spicy-herbaceous 'garrigue' and plump ripeness besides; from legendary local winemaker Alain Grignon. Outstanding value.

8 Celliers des Dauphins Réserve des Vignerons Merlot-Grenache 2012 £5.49
A humble 'Vin de France', maybe a bit plebeian for Waitrose, but it's an awfully likeable, sun-baked, Mediterranean, sweetly ripe and balanced, fruity, everyday red at a friendly price.

8 La Rectorie Côtes du Ventoux 2012 £5.59
Consistent bargain is juicily evocative of new-squashed blackberries with sunny hedgerow spice.

8 Cuvée des Vignerons Beaujolais £5.99
Crisply juicy, dependable non-vintage perennial likes to be chilled.

RED WINES

FRANCE

Waitrose

🍷 8 Waitrose Reserve Claret 2011 £5.99
Modern, upfront-fruit Bordeaux with a lick of toffee amid the ripe cherry-blackberry pure-Merlot fruit.

🍷 8 Waitrose Beaujolais 2011 £6.99
Still very fresh and eager in autumn 2013 – worth trying if it has not been superseded by elusive 2012 vintage; edgy, and good with food.

🍷 8 Domaine des Trois Pierres Costières de Nîmes 2012 £7.49
Sweetly ripe but by no means jammy Gard red in the proper purple, peppery style of the AC; big, focused flavours and 14% alcohol.

🍷 8 Riviera Malbec 2011 £7.99
Colour and fruit of impressive density in this dark, chewy and brambly food red from far southwest France; ripplingly muscular rather than tough or bitter, in the way of good Malbec.

🍷 9 Saumur Les Nivières 2011 £7.99
Bright, crunchily fresh and leafy Loire Cabernet Franc is on top form for the umpteenth vintage in a row; ripe and juicy, it is extra-scrummy with a gentle chill on it.

🍷 9 Jean-Luc Baldès Malbec du Clos 2011 £8.29
It's a Cahors, from the famed Lot Valley AC, and the darkness of the wine is a clue; fruit-packed, roasty-spicy serious wine, a lot more interesting than most of the stuff I've lately tried from this re-emerging location.

RED WINES

8 **Laurent Miquel Vendanges Nocturnes**
   Merlot/Cabernet Sauvignon 2012   **£8.49**
Lots of vineyards, even in Europe, pick at night to minimise spontaneous fermentation in the grapes, but few boast about it in naming the wine; this one does, and I warmed to its sleek Bordeaux style, with extra ripeness and spice.

8 **Bouchard Aîné et Fils Red Burgundy 2011** **£9.99**
Fleshy summer-fruit blend of Pinot Noir and Gamay has likeable squashed-raspberry juiciness, but length of flavour too.

10 **Georges Duboeuf Chiroubles 2011**   **£9.99**
Deep-purple colour in this florally labelled Beaujolais cru attracts you to the characteristic raspberry perfume, laced with a big whiff of violets; fruit is firm, structural and satisfying, with an easy tannin grip suggesting the wine will evolve for years yet.

8 **Rémy Ferbras Rasteau 2012**   **£9.99**
Rasteau is an individual AC village of the southern Rhône, and one to watch for intensely, warmingly spicy-savoury deep-purple Grenache-Syrah blends like this; 15% alcohol.

8 **Baron des Tours 2011**   **£10.49**
Médoc Merlot-Cabernets blend has nice weight and balance in this new vintage, aspiring to the standards of the memorable 2009; fine stalwart Bordeaux with a bitter-chocolate centre.

FRANCE

RED WINES

FRANCE

Waitrose

8 **Cuvée Balthazar Syrah 2011** £11.99
Posh Pays d'Oc is smooth (but unoaked) and sophisticated
in a dark sort of way with a bitter-herb black-fruit savour
familiar from appellations such as St Chinian; 14%
alcohol. Not cheap, but it grows on you.

9 **Domaine de la Croix de Chaintres Saumur
Champigny 2012** £11.99
Handsomely presented Loire classic by the Filliatreau
family, leading producers in Saumur, is purply bright with
lush stalky-fresh red-berry fruits making long, cohesive
flavours with a gently gripping finish.

8 **Domaine Paul Blanck Pinot Noir 2011** £14.99
A rare bird from Alsace, a distinctively leafy, fresh and
crunchy dry red with proper Pinot summer-fruit ripeness
to drink cool with salads.

7 **Château Cambon La Pelouse 2007** £18.99
Haut-Médoc from an under-rated and now maturing
vintage is dense, browning but still grippy, and brimming
with proper cedary claret flavours; almost worth the
money.

8 **Domaine du Grapillon d'Or Gigondas
2011** £18.99
Serious southern Rhône Grenache-Syrah feels long aged
and seasoned, even though only just out of its year in old
oak casks; grandly bottled, lavish, gamey-spicy smoothie
with 14.5% alcohol.

RED WINES

FRANCE

🍷 8 **Arc du Rhône Châteauneuf du Pape 2011 £19.99**
If I say it's good of its kind I intend no aspersion; this is
lovely, slinky, nuanced, spicy, already mellow red wine
in its Châteauneuf-du-Pape sort of way; price is not
outrageous.

🍷 8 **Croix de Beaucaillou 2009**   **£50.00**
This is the 'second wine' of legendary and ludicrously
priced 'second growth' St Julien Château Ducru-
Beaucaillou, and I suppose I should be grateful to taste it.
It's gorgeous, and nearly old enough to drink. For show-
offs, a good investment, I suppose. Wine Direct.

🍷 6 **Waitrose Rich and Intense Italian Red**   **£4.99**
Non-vintage Puglian medley is indeed red, but neither
rich nor intense in the ways I imagine might have been
hoped for, I fear. Disappointing.

ITALY

🍷 8 **Recchia Bardolino 2012**   **£6.99**
Light but not ephemeral Veronese red, long out of
fashion, has poised, even polished, cherry fruit in fine
balance; really rather elegant, and a good one to chill.

🍷 9 **Chianti Cerro del Masso Poggiotondo 2010 £8.99**
Oak-aged riserva-style Chianti at a sensible price cleverly
replicates much more expensive names with rich but vivid
dark fruit and a proper nutskin-dry finish.

🍷 8 **Vinchio-Vaglia I Tre Vescovi Barnera d'Asti
        Superiore 2010**   **£8.99**
Tightly focused blueberry bouncer with juicy appeal and
a lick of luxurious oak works convincingly.

RED WINES

ITALY

9 Chianti Riserva Cecchi Sagrato 2009 £9.99
Seductively lush Chianti has hallmark cherry-blackcurrant
perfume and sleek, plummy, darkly savoury fruit with the
correct gently gripping dry finish; marvellously good.

9 Paolo Leo Primitivo di Manduria 2011 £10.99
Bumper near-black roasty-ripe Puglian red-meat wine has
plenty of savour and 14.5% alcohol; Primitivo grape has
a dark spiciness all its own and is worth discovering.

8 Masi Campofiorin 2009 £12.49
Long-established Verona brand is a sort of super-
Valpolicella, including wine from part-dried grapes then
oak-aged. The effect is a mellow, nutty, even raisiny dark
velvet wine with notions of cloves and cinnamon in the
flavour.

8 Barone Ricasoli Castello di Brolio 2008 £40.00
A long-ago Barone Ricasoli, sometime prime minister
of Italy, devised the Chianti grape formula at his Brolio
estate. Nice story, and this is a lovely wine, which it needs
to be at the price. The bottle is extremely heavy – beware.

NEW ZEALAND

9 Escarpment The Edge Pinot Noir 2012 £13.99
From Martinborough, Kiwi capital of Pinot, this lush,
green-tinged, silky summer-fruit food wine (roast chicken
will do nicely) is worth the price.

**9 Craggy Range Gimblett Gravels Vineyard
Syrah 2010** £18.99
'Lush, pure, even mineral,' I wrote cryptically in my note
on this Hawke's Bay Syrah. I added 'Perfection' and left it
at that. You'll just have to take my word for it.

RED WINES

N. ZEALAND

9 **Mountford Village Pinot Noir 2009** £27.99
Price notwithstanding, I must include this pale, shapely
Waipara wine because it is the best Kiwi Pinot I have
tasted all year. Ineffably delicious and 14.5% alcohol.
Wine Direct.

PORTUGAL

8 **Tagus Creek Cabernet Sauvignon/Aragones
2011** £6.75
Cabernet accounts for half the blend, but this is a truly
Portuguese-tasting red with dark grip and clovey spice,
distinctive and appealing.

8 **Grão Vasco Dão 2009** £7.99
Defined and darkly intriguing midweight of authentic
Portuguese style made mainly from port grapes Touriga
Nacional and Tinta Roriz grown in the reviving Dão
region.

9 **Tinta da Anfora 2010** £8.49
Perennially sumptuous oaked Alentejo red is as dense in
colour, fruit and savour as ever; plush, spicy and silky
with gentle tannic grip and 14% alcohol.

8 **Waitrose Douro Valley Reserva Quinta
da Rosa 2010** £10.99
Table wine from the Port country of the Douro Valley has
a nice porty-minty pong, controlled cassis sweetness and
dark, gripping fruit, finishing very clean and dry; nicely
judged weight.

RED WINES

ROMANIA

9 La Umbra Merlot 2012   £5.99
I assumed this darkly sleek, black-cherry grippy and bright red was Italian, but it's from Dealul Mare, Romania's principal black-grape-growing region. Genuinely good, and good value too.

SOUTH AFRICA

8 Rustenberg John X Merriman 2010   £13.99
Cape claret, in effect, from Bordeaux grapes in French oak, but plumped up a bit no doubt by the difference in hours of sunshine between, say, St Emilion and Stellenbosch; 14.5% alcohol.

9 Thelema Shiraz 2009   £16.99
Thelema is one of the great vineyards of Stellenbosch and this is a great, boot-black, lavishly briary, spicy and creamy Syrah of memorable character and 14% alcohol. Well done to Waitrose for offering it, even if in only 7 giant stores and/or Wine Direct.

SPAIN

8 Waitrose Vega Ariano Rioja 2011   £6.49
Oaked but brisk blackcurranty-brambly crunchy-clean Rioja at a decent price.

8 Casa Carmela Monastrell 2011   £7.79
Typical baked Yecla red from local Monastrell (Mourvèdre) grapes has a roasty-ripe centre and grippy edge to the fruit. Distinctive.

8 Tierras Coloradas Old Vine Carignan 2011 £11.49
Big, gamey Monsant sunshine red has creamy texture but no oak contact; interesting dark pruny flavours and 14% alcohol.

RED WINES

SPAIN

🍷 9 **Torres Salmos Priorat 2010** £16.99
Dense in colour and intense in its sweet-prune, liquorice, spicy black fruit, this is heady stuff (14.5% alcohol), but made with a light touch (it is a Miguel Torres enterprise) that provides a relatively affordable intro to the fabled wines of Priorat.

🍷 8 **Barefoot Shiraz** £6.99
Sunny multi-vintage Californian party wine has a ghastly orange label but ripely appealing juicy-grippy Syrah (I refuse to call it Shiraz) fruit, and a sensible price.

USA

🍷 9 **Bonterra Organic Merlot 2010** £12.99
Bright, summery, black-cherry nose on this dark, coolly minty and poised Californian (Mendocino) food red; Bonterra is the organic tip of the giant Fetzer iceberg, and Merlot an outré grape thanks to the *Sideways* (movie) effect, but this is a meritorious wine.

🍷 8 **Hahn Winery Pinot Noir 2011** £12.99
Characteristically ripe and rich Monterey Pinot of plump summer-pudding fruits but keen acidity, with 14.5% alcohol, is true to the Californian style.

PINK WINES

ARGENTINA

🍷 8 **Finca Flichman Malbec Rosé 2012** £7.99
Plenty of soft summer-fruit with a crisp edge in this full, dry, food pink. It comes from high-altitude Mendoza vineyards, and that somehow emerges in the style of this likeable refresher.

PINK WINES

FRANCE

8 Domaine de Sainte Rose Coquille d'Oc Rosé 2012   £7.49

Laughably named but honourably made Grenache-Syrah Languedoc pink has magenta colour, dry and lively fresh fruit with good balance.

8 Foncaussade Les Parcelles Cabernet Sauvignon/ Merlot Rosé 2012   £7.99

Keen, crisp, red-berry fruit dry wine from Bergerac (neighbour to Bordeaux) has perky salmon-pink colour and good freshness.

ITALY

7 Vignale Pinot Grigio Rosé Blush 2012   £5.99

I blush a bit to suggest this very pale Veneto confection, but as it's both pink and PG I guess it's bound to succeed; flowery nose, hint of hedgerow fruit and off-dry.

SPAIN

8 Waitrose Ripe and Juicy Spanish Rosé 2012   £4.99

From the productive if not distinguished Campo de Borja region, a party-frock-pink Garnacha with a sweet raspberry honk but a certain keen soft-summer-fruit freshness.

8 Marquesa de la Cruz Garnacha Rosé 2012   £6.99

Shocking-pink varietal with softer fruit than some, but plenty of it; good, fresh, lively, dry food wine for tricky menus; 14% alcohol.

8 Muga Rioja Rosé 2012   £9.79

This is about as much as you want to spend on rosé; it does have some Rioja character (though no oak, of course) with strawberry sweetness and a balancing lemon twang at the finish.

WHITE WINES

ARGENTINA

🍷 8 **Catena Chardonnay 2012**　　　　　£12.99
Lemon-gold colour and butterscotch richness in this apple-pie dry wine with brisk citrus edge.

AUSTRALIA

🍷 8 **Wickham Hill Chardonnay 2012**　　　　£6.99
Simple, soft, peachy, oaked everyday refresher finishes clean and brisk.

🍷 8 **Craigmoor Estate Sauvignon Blanc 2012**　£8.99
Fully fruity variation on a now-universal theme has long, lush flavours.

🍷 8 **Tamar Ridge Estate Grown Limited Release Botrytis Riesling 2011 37.5cl**　　　£13.99
The name doesn't leave much to say but it's deep gold, beautifully brûlée and a lot better balanced than a Tasmanian Devil; 9.5% alcohol.

AUSTRIA

🍷 8 **Domaene Gobelsburg Grüner Veltliner 2012**　　　　　　　　　£9.99
At once crisp, and mineral, and ripe with sunny white fruits, this is intriguing and satisfying; ace introduction to the under-appreciated wines of Austria.

🍷 9 **Rabl Schenkenbichl Riesling Reserve 2011** £20.99
At last, an Austrian wine that's not Grüner Veltliner; it's a fabulously racy but rich classic Riesling with exotic fruit memories including nectarine and pineapple; extravagantly delicious and 14% alcohol. Wine Direct.

WHITE WINES

CHILE

🍷 **8** **Waitrose Chilean Sauvignon Blanc 2012** £7.99
Soft, unchallenging style, but it's by no means flabby or spongy; in fact, it grew on me; ripe, grassy and satisfyingly long. It is made, disturbingly, by a New Zealander.

🍷 **8** **Cuvée Pêcheur 2012** £4.95
Brassica-brisk dry refresher from (I believe) Gascony is a bargain and a modest 11.5% alcohol.

🍷 **10** **Cave de Lugny Mâcon-Villages Chardonnay 2012** £7.99
Slurpable fresh tropical-fruit dry wine from estimable Cave de Lugny co-operative is a flagship for the lovable and still sensibly priced burgundies of the Mâconnais; this has been made without oak contact but is nevertheless rich, even honeyed.

FRANCE

🍷 **8** **Champteloup Chardonnay 2012** £7.99
Amiable oddity from the Loire has cabbagey crispness and apple freshness with a cool, mineral quality to the whole package; this sort of thing could catch on.

🍷 **8** **Fief Guérin Muscadet Sur Lie Côtes de Grandlieu 2012** £7.99
More fruit than I'd expected from this famously green and austere Loire appellation; good brisk match for shellfish.

🍷 **9** **Waitrose Sauvignon Blanc 2012** £7.99
Really tangy focused grassy flavours in this Touraine (Loire Valley) rush-of-fruit refresher; even in the face of competition from grander regional appellations, not to mention New Zealand, this stands out.

WHITE WINES

FRANCE

8 **Waitrose White Burgundy 2011** £8.49
Nice lemon-gold Mâconnais has sweet-apple Chardonnay fruit in a racy, near-austere rush, artfully enriched with oak contact.

8 **Cave de Türckheim Gewürztraminer 2012** £9.99
Ubiquitous Alsace wine seems to me an improvement on other recent vintages; proper rose-petal perfume, almost delicate in its lychee and spiced fruit, and fresher, less cloying than before. Rather good, in fact.

8 **Cave de Beblenheim Grafenreben Riesling 2010** £9.99
Aromatic Alsace wine is a fruit salad of zesty orchard flavours and quite dry; don't expect anything like German Riesling, but do expect to be delighted.

9 **Cave de Viré Les Grandes Plantes 2011** £10.49
From the Mâconnais AC of Viré-Clessé, an apple-pie Chardonnay of minerality and long, long flavours; no oak, but no lack of intensity and richness; a lovely natural wine.

8 **Clos de Nouys Vouvray Demi-Sec 2012** £11.99
'Demi-Sec' makes it sounds sweeter than it is. This is a lush, pineapple-juicy, discreetly honeyed Loire Chenin Blanc with verve and freshness. Classy aperitif.

10 **Jurançon Château Jolys Cuvée Jean 2010** £14.49
More than 200 wines in on the day of the Waitrose tasting, I was a bit jaded by the time I got to this Pyrenean sweetie; the effect was galvanising: pure gold, beautifully balanced nectar for aperitif sipping or with a nibble of blue cheese. My top sweet wine of the year.

WHITE WINES

FRANCE

🍷 8 **Domaine Masson-Blandelet Pouilly-Fumé 2012**   £14.99

Regal Loire Sauvignon has racy fresh green fruit relieved with a saucy blanched-almond richness; poised, balanced, elegant and expensive.

GERMANY

🍷 8 **Dr Loosen Urziger Würzgarten Riesling Kabinett 2012**   £15.99

Textbook moselle is so fresh and zingy it's nearly spritzy; delicate honeyed but crisp sweet-apple racy Riesling with just 8% alcohol.

🍷 9 **Weingut Göttelmann Münsterer Dautenpflänzer Riesling Auslese 2010 50cl**   £24.99

Deliriously exciting apple-sweet, honeyed, but racy Nahe wine with crystal river freshness is an experience to taste, if you're into that sort of thing (as I am, when someone else is paying); 8% alcohol. Wine Direct.

HUNGARY

🍷 7 **Waitrose Hungarian Pinot Grigio 2012**   £5.99

If it sounds unappealing, don't be put off: this is no worse than most Italian PG; it's soft but not wet, and even has a whisper of crisp fruit and smoky spice.

ITALY

🍷 8 **Vignale Soave 2012**   £4.99

For the money, absolutely fine; fresh, greenish, with clean edge and 11.5% alcohol.

🍷 9 **Alasia Cortese 2012**   £5.69

This is Gavi, from Piedmont, by another name and it's delicious, with a sort of sweet-nut richness to the dry, delicate orchard fruit; enticing, just 11.5% alcohol, and cheap.

WHITE WINES

 8 **Zenato Villa Flora Lugana 2012** £8.99
Perpetual Veneto brand cunningly combines field freshness with orchard fruit and blanched-almond creaminess. Endearing dry and deeply Italian white.

8 **LaVis Vigneti di Montagna Pinot Grigio 2012** £9.49
Well above the bog standard for Italian PG. In fact, it tastes nothing like most Italian PG. From sub-alpine Trentino it's generously coloured, ripe with crisp-apple fruit (bit of clove here too) and spice on the way to a tangy citrus finish.

8 **Malvira Roero Arneis 2012** £10.99
Piedmont's prestige white grape, the Roero Arneis, is on form in this family-estate dry wine with lush nuttiness and tropical tendencies trimmed with dry, mineral texture. Grand.

8 **Soave Classico Inama Vigneti di Foscarino 2011** £18.99
For those nostalgic for once-fashionable Soave, a richly coloured, fino-sherry-nosed, archly fruity but white-nut leesy wine of the old school.

8 **Crociani Vin Santo di Montepulciano 2005 37.5cl** £19.49
Tuscanophiles pining for vin santo could try this tan-coloured, oloroso-like, gorgeously intense old vintage; terrific – and terrifically expensive.

WHITE WINES

9 Waitrose Sauvignon Blanc 2012 £7.99
Oddly, 15% of this Marlborough wine is Chardonnay,
but the formula works: lashings of crisp gooseberry and
grassy long-flavoured archetypal Kiwi Sauvignon; rivals
the big brands for quality and certainly for value.

**8 Forrest Estate The Doctors' Sauvignon Blanc
2012** £8.99
Experimental wine with natural 9.5% alcohol is a little
bit sharp but still pleasingly fruity and zesty in the proper
Kiwi manner.

9 Wither Hills Pinot Gris 2012 £10.49
Artfully made by one of the great wineries of
Marlborough, this follows the Alsace style for Pinot Gris,
so it's aromatic, intense, smoky, spicy and rich; add in
the Kiwi minerality and vivacity of fruit and you have a
special wine.

8 Quinta de Azevedo Vinho Verde 2012 £7.49
This Sogrape (Mateus/Sandeman etc.) brand is bracingly
dry and tangy and really quite authentic; will it revive the
fashion for vinho verde? Just 11% alcohol.

8 Puklavec & Friends Sauvignon Blanc 2012 £8.99
I am very pleased to see this newcomer from last year
back with another vintage; again, it's gooseberry-
bright and grassy-fresh with plenty of interest from the
immortally named vineyards of Kog, Vinski Vrh and Mali
Brebrovnik.

NEW ZEALAND

PORTUGAL

SLOVENIA

WHITE WINES

S. AFRICA

8 **Zalze Bush Vines Chenin Blanc 2012**　　£7.99
Nutty-rich with a hint of honeysuckle and yet zingy, fresh and entirely dry at the finish; distinctive aperitif or white-meat wine with 14% alcohol.

SPAIN

10 **Waitrose Aromatic and Citrus Spanish Dry White 2012**　　£4.99
A cumbersome name, maybe, but a simply delicious brisk and breezy wine from a cunning blend of Airen and Verdejo grapes; the effect is electric, a proper exciting Atlantic-fresh style at a giveaway price.

9 **Waitrose Libra Verdejo 2012**　　£7.99
Tangy, nearly tart, fresh green-fruit dry and grassy thriller from the inspiring Verdejo grape made in Rueda; this wine has all its ducks in a proverbial row.

8 **Cune Barrel Fermented Rioja 2012**　　£9.99
You don't get a lot of white Rioja, and the old-fashioned oaked kind is near extinct; this is a modern fresh wine, but wickedly creamy and nutty; lavish fun. Try with gambas.

FORTIFIED WINES

PORTUGAL

9 Waitrose Ruby Port   £7.49
Cleverly contrived, sweet-but-balanced, silky, long, dark plum and fig flavours; remarkably well unified young wine with 19% alcohol, and a bargain at this price.

8 Sandeman Late-Bottled Vintage Port 2008 £15.75
Standout LBV from enormous but elusive Sandeman is dark as the Don's cape, full of plummy savour and comforting richness; 20.5% alcohol.

SPAIN

10 Waitrose Amontillado Sherry   £6.99
Brilliant sherry by Sanchez Romate, a long-term and independent supplier to Waitrose, this is a very slightly sweetened dry amontillado of fabulous quality for the money; chestnut brown, polished nutty-figgy fruit, healthily fresh and 18.5% alcohol. Drink it properly chilled, and cry Viva Jerez!

9 Waitrose Cream Sherry   £6.99
It's dry, really, by which I mean it's real sherry, because all proper sherry is fermented out before fortification so has no residual sugar. But never mind that. This is fruit-cake rich, poised and balanced, sublimely stimulating to mind and palate, good value and 19.5% alcohol. Drink chilled.

**8 Waitrose Solera Jerezana Dry Oloroso
Sherry**   £9.75
Made by Lustau, it's nut brown, strongly aromatic with fig, date, prune and walnut notes and indeed dry; drink cool (yes, even brown sherry likes a chill) with cheese or nuts; 20% alcohol.

SPARKLING WINES

ENGLAND

🍷 **8** **Jenkyn Place Brut 2008** £21.99
Lemony entry into really attractive champagne-style vigorous sparkler from Hampshire is competently followed up with vivid fruit and correct balance; it's the real thing.

🍷 **10** **Camel Valley Pinot Noir Brut 2010** £27.99
This Cornish vineyard now produces seriously good champagne-style wines with complete consistency, year after year. This one is impressively ripe, nearly tropical in its fruitiness, though properly polished and crisp; it just tastes absolutely right and you don't have to be British, I'd venture, to think it's as good as any sparkler at the price – even a price as high as this.

FRANCE

🍷 **8** **Cave de Lugny Crémant de Bourgogne** £12.99
It's a blanc de blancs, all Chardonnay, and you get lots of crisp-apple fruit with bready aromas and lively zest; 11.5% alcohol.

🍷 **8** **Waitrose Brut Special Reserve Vintage Champagne 2004** £30.99
You have to put a lot of trust in a supermarket to fork out £30 for an own-label wine, but in this case it will pay off; lovely toasty rich mellow-with-bottle-age Heidsieck-made golden oldie with long, seductive fruit.

🍷 **8** **Pol Roger Pure Extra Brut** £42.99
I do think it's important to keep up with how the grande marque champagnes are doing, ho-ho; this brazen luxury brand is brazenly luxurious; if you can afford it, you'll probably like it.

SPARKLING WINES

🍷 8 San Leo Asti   £9.49
This is a quality Asti 'spumante' with honeyed rather
than candied sweetness and an endearing freshness and
liveliness. Jolly nice cake wine, and just 7% alcohol.

🍷 8 Rosamore Spumante Rosato   £9.99
Pale rose pink with a sweetish floral nose, but it's better
than I expected: fully frothy, keen fresh strawberry fruit,
lively zest; an amiable fizz from Garganega (as in Soave)
grapes coloured with Negroamaro; 10.5% alcohol.

—Making the most of it—

There has always been a lot of nonsense talked about the correct ways to serve wine. Red wine, we are told, should be opened and allowed to 'breathe' before pouring. White wine should be chilled. Wine doesn't go with soup, tomatoes or chocolate. You know the sort of thing.

It would all be simply laughable except that these daft conventions do make so many potential wine lovers nervous about the simple ritual of opening a bottle and sharing it around. Here is a short and opinionated guide to the received wisdom.

Breathing

Simply uncorking a wine for an hour or two before you serve it will make absolutely no difference to the way it tastes. However, if you wish to warm up an icy bottle of red by placing it near (never on) a radiator or fire, do remove the cork first. As the wine warms, even very slightly, it gives off gas, which will spoil the flavour if it cannot escape.

Chambré-ing

One of the more florid terms in the wine vocabulary. The idea is that red wine should be at the same temperature as the room (chambre) you're going to drink it in. In fairness, it makes sense – although the term harks back to the days when the only people who drank wine were those who could afford to keep it in the freezing cold vaulted cellars beneath their houses. The ridiculously high temperatures to which some homes are raised by central heating systems today are really far too warm for wine. But presumably those who live in such circumstances do so out of choice, and will prefer their wine to be similarly overheated.

Chilling

Drink your white wine as cold as you like. It's certainly true that good whites are at their best at a cool rather than at an icy temperature, but cheap and characterless wines can be improved immeasurably if they are cold enough – the anaesthetising effect of the temperature removes all sense of taste. Pay no attention to notions that red wine should not be served cool. There are plenty of lightweight reds that will respond very well to an hour in the fridge.

Corked wine

Wine trade surveys reveal that far too many bottles are in no fit state to be sold. The villain is very often cited as the cork. Cut from the bark of cork-oak trees cultivated for the purpose in Portugal and Spain, these natural stoppers have done sterling service for 200 years, but now face a crisis of confidence among wine producers. A diseased or damaged cork can make the wine taste stale because air has penetrated, or musty-mushroomy due to TCA, an infection of the raw material. These faults in wine, known as 'corked' or 'corky', should be immediately obvious, even in the humblest bottle, so you should return the bottle to the supplier and demand a refund.

Today, more and more wine producers are opting to close their bottles with polymer bungs. Some are designed to resemble the 'real thing' while others come in a rather disorienting range of colours – including black. While these things can be a pain to extract, there seems to be no evidence they do any harm to the wine. Don't 'lay down' bottles closed with polymer. The potential effects of years of contact with the plastic are yet to be scientifically established.

The same goes for screwcaps. These do have the merit of obviating the struggle with the corkscrew, but prolonged contact of the plastic liner with the wine might not be a good idea.

Corkscrews

The best kind of corkscrew is the 'waiter's friend' type. It looks like a pen-knife, unfolding a 'worm' (the helix or screw) and a lever device which, after the worm has been driven into the cork (try to centre it) rests on the lip of the bottle and enables you to withdraw the cork with minimal effort. Some have two-stage lips to facilitate the task. These devices are cheaper and longer-lasting than any of the more elaborate types, and are equally effective at withdrawing polymer bungs – which can be hellishly difficult to unwind from Teflon-coated 'continuous' corkscrews like the Screwpull.

Decanting

There are two views on the merits of decanting wines. The prevailing one seems to be that it is pointless and even pretentious. The other is that it can make real improvements in the way a wine tastes and is definitely worth the trouble.

Scientists, not usually much exercised by the finer nuances of wine, will tell you that exposure to the air causes wine to 'oxidise' – take in oxygen molecules that will quite quickly initiate the process of turning wine into vinegar – and anyone who has tasted a 'morning-after' glass of wine will no doubt vouch for this.

But the fact that wine does oxidise is a genuine clue to the reality of the effects of exposure to air. Shut inside its bottle, a young wine is very much a live substance, jumping with natural, but mysterious, compounds that can cause all sorts of strange taste sensations. But by exposing the wine to air these effects are markedly reduced.

In wines that spend longer in the bottle, the influence of these factors diminishes, in a process called 'reduction'. In red wines, the hardness of tannin – the natural preservative imparted into wine from the grape skins – gradually reduces, just as the raw purple colour darkens to ruby and later to orangey-brown.

I believe there is less reason for decanting old wines than new, unless the old wine has thrown a deposit and needs carefully to be poured off it. And in some light-bodied wines, such as older Rioja, decanting is probably a bad idea because it can accelerate oxidation all too quickly.

As to actual experiments, I have carried out several of my own, with wines opened in advance or wines decanted compared to the same wines just opened and poured, and my own unscientific judgement is that big, young, alcoholic reds can certainly be improved by aeration.

Washing glasses

If your wine glasses are of any value to you, don't put them in the dishwasher. Over time, they'll craze from the heat of the water. And they will not emerge in the glitteringly pristine condition suggested by the pictures on some detergent packets. For genuinely perfect glasses that will stay that way, wash them in hot soapy water, rinse with clean, hot water and dry immediately with a glass cloth kept exclusively for this purpose. Sounds like fanaticism, but if you take your wine seriously, you'll see there is sense in it.

Keeping wine

How long can you keep an opened bottle of wine before it goes downhill? Not long. A re-corked bottle with just a glassful out of it should stay fresh until the day after, but if there is a lot of air inside the bottle, the wine will oxidise, turning progressively stale and sour. Wine 'saving' devices that allow you to withdraw the air from the bottle via a punctured, self-sealing rubber stopper are variably effective, but don't expect these to keep a wine fresh for more than a couple of re-openings. A crafty method of keeping a half-finished bottle is to decant it, via a funnel, into a clean half bottle and recork.

Storing wine

Supermarket labels always seem to advise that 'this wine should be consumed within one year of purchase'. I think this is a wheeze to persuade customers to drink it up quickly and come back for more. Many of the more robust red wines are likely to stay in good condition for much more than one year, and plenty will actually improve with age. On the other hand, it is a sensible axiom that inexpensive dry white wines are better the younger they are. If you do intend to store wines for longer than a few weeks, do pay heed to the conventional wisdom that bottles are best stored in low, stable temperatures, preferably in the dark. Bottles closed with conventional corks should be laid on their side lest the corks dry out for lack of contact with the wine. But one of the notable advantages of the new closures now proliferating is that if your wine comes with a polymer 'cork' or a screwcap, you can safely store it upright.

Wine and food

Wine is made to be drunk with food, but some wines go better with particular dishes than others. It is no coincidence that Italian wines, characterised by soft, cherry fruit and a clean, mouth-drying finish, go so well with the sticky delights of pasta.

But it's personal taste rather than national associations that should determine the choice of wine with food. And if you prefer a black-hearted Argentinian Malbec to a brambly Italian Barbera with your Bolognese, that's fine.

The conventions that have grown up around wine and food pairings do make some sense, just the same. I was thrilled to learn in the early days of my drinking career that sweet, dessert wines can go well with strong blue cheese. As I don't much like puddings, but love sweet wines, I was eager to test this match – and I'm here to tell you that it works very well indeed as the end-piece to a grand meal in which there is cheese as well as pud on offer.

Red wine and cheese are supposed to be a natural match, but I'm not so sure. Reds can taste awfully tinny with soft cheeses such as Brie and Camembert, and even worse with goat's cheese. A really extravagant, yellow Australian Chardonnay will make a better match. Hard cheeses such as Cheddar and the wonderful Old Amsterdam (top-of-the-market Gouda) are better with reds.

And then there's the delicate issue of fish. Red wine is supposed to be a no-no. This might well be true of grilled and wholly unadorned white fish, such as sole or a delicate dish of prawns, scallops or crab. But what about oven-roasted monkfish or a substantial winter-season fish pie? An edgy red will do very well indeed, and provide much comfort for those many among us who simply prefer to drink red wine with food, and white wine on its own.

It is very often the method by which dishes are prepared, rather than their core ingredients, that determines which wine will work best. To be didactic, I would always choose Beaujolais or summer-fruit-style reds such as those from Pinot Noir grapes to go with a simple roast chicken. But if the bird is cooked as coq au vin with a hefty wine sauce, I would plump for a much more assertive red.

Some sauces, it is alleged, will overwhelm all wines. Salsa and curry come to mind. I have carried out a number of experiments into this great issue of our time, in my capacity as consultant to a company that specialises in supplying wines to Asian restaurants. One discovery I have made is that forcefully fruity dry white wines with keen acidity can go very well indeed even with fairly incendiary dishes. Sauvignon Blanc with Madras? Give it a try!

I'm also convinced, however, that some red wines will stand up very well to a bit of heat. The marvellously robust reds of Argentina made from Malbec grapes are good partners to Mexican chilli-hot recipes and salsa dishes. The dry, tannic edge to these wines provides a good counterpoint to the inflammatory spices in the food.

Some foods are supposedly impossible to match with wine. Eggs and chocolate are among the prime offenders. And yet, legendary cook Elizabeth David's best-selling autobiography was entitled *An Omelette and a Glass of Wine*, and the affiliation between chocolates and champagne is an unbreakable one. Taste is, after all, that most personally governed of all senses. If your choice is a boiled egg washed down with a glass of claret, who is to dictate otherwise?

What wine
——————words mean——————

Wine labels are getting crowded. It's mostly thanks to the unending torrent of new regulation. Lately, for example, the European Union has decided that all wines sold within its borders must display a health warning: 'Contains Sulphites'. All wines are made with the aid of preparations containing sulphur to combat diseases in the vineyards and bacterial infections in the winery. You can't make wine without sulphur. Even 'organic' wines are made with it. But some people are sensitive to the traces of sulphur in some wines, so we must all be informed of the presence of this hazardous material.

That's the way it is. And it might not be long before some even sterner warnings will be added about another ingredient in wine. Alcohol is the new tobacco, as the regulators see it, and in the near future we can look forward to some stern admonishments about the effects of alcohol. In the meantime, the mandatory information on every label includes the quantity, alcoholic strength and country of origin, along with the name of the producer. The region will be specified, vaguely on wines from loosely regulated countries such as Australia, and precisely on wines from over-regulated countries such as France. Wines from 'classic' regions of Europe – Bordeaux, Chianti, Rioja and so on – are mostly labelled according to their location rather than their constituent grape varieties. If it says Sancerre, it's taken as read that you either know it's made with Sauvignon Blanc grapes, or don't care.

Wines from just about everywhere else make no such assumptions. If a New Zealand wine is made from Sauvignon Blanc grapes, you can be sure the label will say so. This does quite neatly represent the gulf between the two worlds of winemaking. In traditional European regions, it's the place, the vineyard, that mostly determines the character of the wines. The French call it *terroir*, to encapsulate not just the lie of the land and the soil conditions but the wild variations in the weather from year to year as well. The grapes are merely the medium through which the timeless mysteries of the deep earth are translated into the ineffable glories of the wine, adjusted annually according to the vagaries of climate, variable moods of the winemaker, and who knows what else.

In the less arcane vineyards of the New World, the grape is definitely king. In hot valleys such as the Barossa (South Australia) or the Maipo (Chile), climate is relatively predictable and the soil conditions are managed by irrigation. It's the fruit that counts, and the style of the wine is determined by the variety – soft, spicy Shiraz; peachy, yellow Chardonnay and so on.

The main purpose of this glossary is, consequently, to give short descriptions of the 'classic' wines, including the names of the grapes they are made from, and of the 70-odd distinct grape varieties that make most of the world's wines. As well as these very brief descriptions, I have included equally shortened summaries of the regions and appellations of the better-known wines, along with some of the local terms used to indicate style and alleged qualities.

Finally, I have tried to explain in simple and rational terms the peculiar words I use in trying to convey the characteristics of wines described. 'Delicious' might need no further qualification, but the likes of 'bouncy', 'green' and 'liquorous' probably do.

A

abboccato – Medium-dry white wine style. Italy, especially Orvieto.

AC – *See* Appellation d'Origine Contrôlée.

acidity – To be any good, every wine must have the right level of acidity. It gives wine the element of dryness or sharpness it needs to prevent cloying sweetness or dull wateriness. If there is too much acidity, wine tastes raw or acetic (vinegary). Winemakers strive to create balanced acidity – either by cleverly controlling the natural processes, or by adding sugar and acid to correct imbalances.

aftertaste – The flavour that lingers in the mouth after swallowing the wine.

Aglianico – Black grape variety of southern Italy. It has romantic associations. When the ancient Greeks first colonised Italy in the seventh century BC, it was with the prime purpose of planting it as a vineyard (the Greek name for Italy was *Oenotria* – land of cultivated vines). The name for the vines the Greeks brought with them was Ellenico (as in Hellas, Greece), from which Aglianico is the modern rendering. To return to the point, these ancient vines, especially in the arid volcanic landscapes of Basilicata and Cilento, produce excellent dark, earthy and highly distinctive wines. A name to look out for.

Agriculture biologique – On French wine labels, an indication that the wine has been made by organic methods.

Albariño – White grape variety of Spain that makes intriguingly perfumed fresh and spicy dry wines, especially in esteemed Rias Baixas region.

alcohol – The alcohol levels in wines are expressed in terms of alcohol by volume ('abv'), that is, the percentage of the volume of the wine that is common, or ethyl, alcohol. A typical wine at 12 per cent abv is thus 12 parts alcohol and, in effect, 88 parts fruit juice.

The question of how much alcohol we can drink without harming ourselves in the short or long term is an impossible one to answer, but there is more or less general agreement among scientists that small amounts of alcohol are good for us, even if the only evidence of this is actuarial – the fact that mortality statistics show teetotallers live significantly shorter lives than moderate drinkers. According to the Department of Health, there are 'safe limits' to the amount of alcohol we should drink weekly. These limits are measured in units of alcohol, with a small glass of wine taken to be one unit. Men are advised that 28 units a week is the most they can drink without risk to health, and for women (whose liver function differs from that of men because of metabolic distinctions) the figure is 21 units.

If you wish to measure your consumption closely, note that a standard 75 cl bottle of wine at 12 per cent alcohol contains 9 units. A bottle of German Moselle at 8 per cent alcohol has only 6 units, but a bottle of Australian Chardonnay at 14 per cent has 10.5.

Alentejo – Wine region of southern Portugal (immediately north of the Algarve), with a fast-improving reputation, especially for sappy, keen reds from local grape varieties including Aragones, Castelão and Trincadeira.

Almansa – DO winemaking region of Spain inland from Alicante, making great-value red wines.

Alsace – France's easternmost wine-producing region lies between the Vosges Mountains and the River Rhine, with Germany beyond. These conditions make for the production of some of the world's most delicious and fascinating white wines, always sold under the name of their constituent grapes. Pinot Blanc is the most affordable – and is well worth looking out for. The 'noble' grape varieties of the region are Gewürztraminer, Muscat, Riesling and Pinot Gris and they are always made on a single-variety basis. The richest, most exotic wines are those from individual *grand cru* vineyards, which are named on the label. Some *vendange tardive* (late harvest) wines are made, but tend to be expensive. All the wines are sold in tall, slim green bottles known as flûtes that closely resemble those of the Mosel, and the names of producers and grape varieties are often German too, so it is widely assumed that Alsace wines are German in style, if not in nationality. But this is not the case in either particular. Alsace wines are dry and quite unique in character – and definitely French.

Amarone – Style of red wine made in Valpolicella, Italy. Specially selected grapes are held back from the harvest and stored for several months to dry them out. They are then pressed and fermented into a highly concentrated speciality dry wine. Amarone means 'bitter', describing the dry style of the flavour.

amontillado – *See* sherry.

aperitif – If a wine is thus described, I believe it will give more pleasure before a meal than with one. Crisp, low-alcohol German wines and other delicately flavoured whites (including many dry Italians) are examples.

Appellation d'Origine Contrôlée – Commonly abbreviated to AC or AOC, this is the system under which quality wines are defined in France. About a third of the country's vast annual output qualifies, and there are more than 400 distinct AC zones. The declaration of an AC on the label signifies that the wine meets standards concerning location of vineyards and wineries, grape varieties and limits on harvest per hectare, methods of cultivation and vinification, and alcohol content. Wines are inspected and tasted by state-appointed committees. The one major aspect of any given wine that an AC cannot guarantee is that you will like it – but it certainly improves the chances.

Appellation d'Origine Protégée (AOP) – Under recent EU rule changes, the AOC system is gradually transforming into AOP. In effect, it will mean little more than the exchange of 'controlled' with 'protected' on labels. One quirk of the new rules is that makers of AOP wines will be able to name the constituent grape variety or varieties on their labels, if they so wish.

Apulia – Anglicised name for Puglia.

Aragones – Synonym in Portugal, especially in the Alentejo region, for the Tempranillo grape variety of Spain.

Ardèche – Region of southern France to the west of the Rhône valley, home to a good vin de pays zone known as the Coteaux de L'Ardèche. Lots of decent-value reds from Syrah grapes, and some, less interesting, dry whites.

Arneis – White grape variety of Piedmont, north-west Italy. Makes dry whites with a certain almondy richness at often-inflated prices.

Assyrtiko – White grape variety of Greece now commonly named on dry white wines, sometimes of great quality, from the mainland and islands.

Asti – Town and major winemaking centre in Piedmont, Italy. The sparkling (spumante) sweet wines made from Moscato grapes are inexpensive and often delicious. Typical alcohol level is a modest 5 to 7 per cent.

attack – In wine tasting, the first impression made by the wine in the mouth.

Auslese – German wine-quality designation. *See* QmP.

B

Baga – Black grape variety indigenous to Portugal. Makes famously concentrated, juicy reds that get their deep colour from the grape's particularly thick skins. Look out for this name, now quite frequently quoted as the varietal on Portuguese wine labels. Often very good value for money.

balance – A big word in the vocabulary of wine tasting. Respectable wine must get two key things right: lots of fruitiness from the sweet grape juice, and plenty of acidity so the sweetness is 'balanced' with the crispness familiar in good dry whites and the dryness that marks out good reds. Some wines are noticeably 'well balanced' in that they have memorable fruitiness and the clean, satisfying 'finish' (last flavour in the mouth) that ideal acidity imparts.

Barbera – Black grape variety originally of Piedmont in Italy. Most commonly seen as Barbera d'Asti, the vigorously fruity red wine made around Asti – once better known for sweet sparkling Asti Spumante. Barbera grapes are now being grown in South America, often producing a sleeker, smoother style than at home in Italy.

Bardolino – Once fashionable, light red wine DOC of Veneto, north-west Italy. Bardolino is made principally from Corvina Veronese grapes plus Rondinella, Molinara and Negrara. Best wines are supposed to be those labelled Bardolino Superiore, a DOCG created in 2002. This classification closely specifies the permissible grape varieties and sets the alcohol level at a minimum of 12 per cent.

Barossa Valley – Famed vineyard region north of Adelaide, Australia, produces hearty reds principally from Shiraz, Cabernet Sauvignon and Grenache grapes, plus plenty of lush white wine from Chardonnay. Also known for limey, long-lived, mineral dry whites from Riesling grapes.

barrique – Barrel in French. *En barrique* on a wine label signifies the wine has been matured in oak.

Beaujolais – Unique red wines from the southern reaches of Burgundy, France, are made from Gamay grapes. Beaujolais nouveau, now deeply unfashionable, provides a friendly introduction to the bouncy, red-fruit style of the wine, but for the authentic experience, go for Beaujolais Villages, from the region's better, northern vineyards. There are ten AC zones within this northern sector making wines under their own names. Known as the *crus*, these are Brouilly, Chénas, Chiroubles, Côte de Brouilly, Fleurie, Juliénas, Morgon, Moulin à Vent, Regnié and St Amour and produce most of the best wines of the region. Prices are higher than those for Beaujolais Villages, but by no means always justifiably so.

Beaumes de Venise – Village near Châteauneuf du Pape in France's Rhône valley, famous for sweet and alcoholic wine from Muscat grapes. Delicious, grapey wines. A small number of growers also make strong (sometimes rather tough) red wines under the village name.

Beaune – One of the two winemaking centres (the other is Nuits St Georges) at the heart of Burgundy in France. Three of the region's humbler appellations take the name of the town: Côtes de Beaune, Côtes de Beaune Villages and Hautes Côtes de Beaune. Wines made under these ACs are often, but by no means always, good value for money.

berry fruit – Some red wines deliver a burst of flavour in the mouth that corresponds to biting into a newly picked berry – strawberry, blackberry, etc. So a wine described as having berry fruit (by this writer, anyway) has freshness, liveliness and immediate appeal.

bianco – White wine, Italy.

Bical – White grape variety principally of Dão region of northern Portugal. Not usually identified on labels, because most of it goes into inexpensive sparkling wines. Can make still wines of very refreshing crispness.

biodynamics – A cultivation method taking the organic approach several steps further. Biodynamic winemakers plant and tend their vineyards according to a date and time calendar 'in harmony' with the movements of the planets. Some of France's best-known wine estates subscribe, and many more are going that way. It might all sound bonkers, but it's salutary to learn that biodynamics is based on principles first described by a very eminent man, the Austrian educationist Rudolph Steiner. He's lately been in the news for having written, in 1919, that farmers crazy enough to feed animal products to cattle would drive the livestock 'mad'.

bite – In wine tasting, the impression on the palate of a wine with plenty of acidity and, often, tannin.

blanc – White wine, France.

blanc de blancs – White wine from white grapes, France. May seem to be stating the obvious, but some white wines (e.g. champagne) are made, partially or entirely, from black grapes.

blanc de noirs – White wine from black grapes, France. Usually sparkling (especially champagne) made from black Pinot Meunier and Pinot Noir grapes, with no Chardonnay or other white varieties.

blanco – White wine, Spain and Portugal.

Blauer Zweigelt – Black grape variety of Austria, making a large proportion of the country's red wines, some of excellent quality.

Bobal – Black grape variety mostly of south-eastern Spain. Thick skin is good for colour and juice contributes acidity to blends.

bodega – In Spain, a wine producer or wine shop.

Bonarda – Black grape variety of northern Italy. Now more widely planted in Argentina, where it makes rather elegant red wines, often representing great value.

botrytis – Full name, *botrytis cinerea*, is that of a beneficent fungus that can attack ripe grape bunches late in the season, shrivelling the berries to a gruesome-looking mess, which yields concentrated juice of prized sweetness. Cheerfully known as 'noble rot', this fungus is actively encouraged by winemakers in regions as diverse as Sauternes (in Bordeaux), Monbazillac (in Bergerac), the Rhine and Mosel valleys, Hungary's Tokaji region and South Australia to make ambrosial dessert wines.

bouncy – The feel in the mouth of a red wine with young, juicy fruitiness. Good Beaujolais is bouncy, as are many north-west-Italian wines from Barbera and Dolcetto grapes.

Bourgogne Grand Ordinaire – Former AC of Burgundy, France. *See* Coteaux Bourguignons.

Bourgueil – Appellation of Loire Valley, France. Long-lived red wines from Cabernet Franc grapes.

briary – In wine tasting, associated with the flavours of fruit from prickly bushes such as blackberries.

brûlé – Pleasant burnt-toffee taste or smell, as in crème brûlée.

brut – Driest style of sparkling wine. Originally French, for very dry champagnes specially developed for the British market, but now used for sparkling wines from all round the world.

Buzet – Little-seen AC of south-west France overshadowed by Bordeaux but producing some characterful ripe reds.

C

Cabardès – AC for red and rosé wines from area north of Carcassonne, Aude, France. Principally Cabernet Sauvignon and Merlot grapes.

Cabernet Franc – Black grape variety originally of France. It makes the light-bodied and keenly edged red wines of the Loire Valley – such as Chinon and Saumur. And it is much grown in Bordeaux, especially in the appellation of St Emilion. Also now planted in Argentina, Australia and North America. Wines, especially in the Loire, are characterised by a leafy, sappy style and bold fruitiness. Most are best enjoyed young.

Cabernet Sauvignon – Black (or, rather, blue) grape variety now grown in virtually every wine-producing nation. When perfectly ripened, the grapes are smaller than many other varieties and have particularly thick skins. This means that when pressed, Cabernet grapes have a high proportion of skin to juice – and that makes for wine with lots of colour and tannin. In Bordeaux, the grape's traditional home, the grandest Cabernet-based wines have always been known as *vins de garde* (wines to keep) because they take years, even decades, to evolve as the effect of all that skin extraction preserves the fruit all the way to magnificent maturity. But in today's impatient world, these grapes are exploited in modern winemaking techniques to produce the sublime flavours of mature Cabernet without having to hang around for lengthy periods awaiting maturation. While there's nothing like a fine, ten-year-old claret (and nothing quite as expensive), there are many excellent Cabernets from around the world that amply illustrate this grape's characteristics. Classic smells and flavours include blackcurrants, cedar wood, chocolate, tobacco – even violets.

Cahors – An AC of the Lot Valley in south-west France once famous for 'black wine'. This was a curious concoction of straightforward wine mixed with a soupy must, made by boiling up new-pressed juice to concentrate it (through evaporation) before fermentation. The myth is still perpetuated that Cahors wine continues to be made in this way, but production on this basis actually ceased 150 years ago. Cahors today is no stronger, or blacker, than the wines of neighbouring appellations.

Cairanne – Village of the appellation collectively known as the Côtes du Rhône in southern France. Cairanne is one of several villages entitled to put their name on the labels of wines made within their AC boundary, and the appearance of this name is quite reliably an indicator of a very good wine indeed.

Calatayud – DO (quality wine zone) near Zaragoza in the Aragon region of northern Spain where they're making some astonishingly good wines at bargain prices, mainly reds from Garnacha and Tempranillo grapes. These are the varieties that go into the light and oaky wines of Rioja, but in Calatayud, the wines are dark, dense and decidedly different.

Cannonau – Black grape native to Sardinia by name, but in fact the same variety as the ubiquitous Grenache of France (and Garnacha of Spain).

cantina sociale – *See* Co-op.

Carignan – Black grape variety of Mediterranean France. It is rarely identified on labels, but is a major constituent of wines from the southern Rhône and

Languedoc-Roussillon regions. Known as Carignano in Italy and Cariñena in Spain.

Cariñena – A region of north-east Spain, south of Navarra, known for substantial reds, as well as the Spanish name for the Carignan grape (*qv*).

Carmenère – Black grape variety once widely grown in Bordeaux but abandoned due to cultivation problems. Lately revived in South America where it is producing fine wines, sometimes with echoes of Bordeaux.

cassis – As a tasting note, signifies a wine that has a noticeable blackcurrant-concentrate flavour or smell. Much associated with the Cabernet Sauvignon grape.

Castelao – Portuguese black grape variety. Same as Periquita.

Catarratto – White grape variety of Sicily. In skilled hands it can make anything from keen, green-fruit dry whites to lush, oaked super-ripe styles. Also used for Marsala.

cat's pee – In tasting notes, a mildly jocular reference to a certain style of Sauvignon Blanc wine.

cava – The sparkling wine of Spain. Most originates in Catalonia, but the Denominación de Origen (DO) guarantee of authenticity is open to producers in many regions of the country. Much cava is very reasonably priced even though it is made by the same method as champagne – second fermentation in bottle, known in Spain as the *método clásico*.

CdR – Côtes du Rhône.

Cépage – Grape variety, French. 'Cépage Merlot' on a label simply means the wine is made largely or exclusively from Merlot grapes.

Chablis – Northernmost AC of France's Burgundy region. Its dry white wines from Chardonnay grapes are known for their fresh and steely style, but the best wines also age very gracefully into complex classics.

Chambourcin – Sounds like a cream cheese but it's a relatively modern (1963) French hybrid black grape that makes some good non-appellation lightweight-but-concentrated reds in the Loire Valley and now some heftier versions in Australia.

Chardonnay – The world's most popular grape variety. Said to originate from the village of Chardonnay in the Mâconnais region of southern Burgundy, the vine is now planted in every wine-producing nation. Wines are commonly characterised by generous colour and sweet-apple smell, but styles range from lean and sharp to opulently rich. Australia started the craze for oaked Chardonnay, the gold-coloured, super-ripe, buttery 'upfront' wines that are a caricature of lavish and outrageously expensive burgundies such as Meursault and Puligny-Montrachet. Rich to the point of egginess, these Aussie pretenders are now giving way to a sleeker, more minerally style with much less oak presence – if any at all. California and Chile, New Zealand and South Africa are competing hard to imitate the Burgundian style, and Australia's success in doing so.

Châteauneuf du Pape – Famed appellation centred on a picturesque village of the southern Rhône valley in France where in the 1320s French Pope Clement V had a splendid new château built for himself as a country retreat amidst his vineyards. The red wines of the AC, which can be made from 13 different grape varieties but principally Grenache, Syrah and Mourvèdre, are regarded as the best of the southern Rhône and have become rather expensive – but they can be sensationally good. Expensive white wines are also made.

Chenin Blanc – White grape variety of the Loire Valley, France. Now also grown farther afield, especially in South Africa. Makes dry, soft white wines and also rich, sweet styles. Sadly, many low-cost Chenin wines are bland and uninteresting.

cherry – In wine tasting, either a pale red colour or, more commonly, a smell or flavour akin to the sun-warmed, bursting sweet ripeness of cherries. Many Italian wines, from lightweights such as Bardolino and Valpolicella to serious Chianti, have this character. 'Black cherry' as a description is often used of Merlot wines – meaning they are sweet but have a firmness associated with the thicker skins of black cherries.

Cinsault – Black grape variety of southern France, where it is invariably blended with others in wines of all qualities ranging from vin de pays to the pricy reds of Châteauneuf du Pape. Also much planted in South Africa. The effect in wine is to add keen aromas (sometimes compared with turpentine!) and softness to the blend. The name is often spelt Cinsaut.

Clape, La – A small *cru* (defined quality-vineyard area) within the Coteaux du Languedoc where the growers make some seriously delicious red wines, mainly from Carignan, Grenache and Syrah grapes. A name worth looking out for on labels from the region.

claret – The red wine of Bordeaux, France. It comes from Latin *clarus*, meaning 'clear', recalling a time when the red wines of the region were much lighter in colour than they are now.

clarete – On Spanish labels indicates a pale-coloured red wine. Tinto signifies a deeper hue.

classed growth – English translation of French *cru classé* describes a group of 60 individual wine estates in the Médoc district of Bordeaux, which in 1855 were granted this new status on the basis that their wines were the most expensive at that time. The classification was a promotional wheeze to attract attention to the Bordeaux stand at that year's Great Exhibition in Paris. Amazingly, all of the 60 wines concerned are still in production and most still occupy more or less their original places in the pecking order price-wise. The league was divided up into five divisions from *Premier Grand Cru Classé* (just four wines originally, with one promoted in 1971 – the only change ever made to the classification) to *Cinquième Grand Cru Classé*. Other regions of Bordeaux, notably Graves and St Emilion, have since imitated Médoc and introduced their own rankings of *cru classé* estates.

classic – An overused term in every respect – wine descriptions being no exception. In this book, the word is used to describe a very good wine of its type. So, a 'classic' Cabernet Sauvignon is one that is recognisably and admirably characteristic of that grape.

Classico – Under Italy's wine laws, this word appended to the name of a DOC zone has an important significance. The classico wines of the region can only be made from vineyards lying in the best-rated areas, and wines thus labelled (e.g. Chianti Classico, Soave Classico, Valpolicella Classico) can be reliably counted on to be a cut above the rest.

Colombard – White grape variety of southern France. Once employed almost entirely for making the wine that is distilled for armagnac and cognac brandies, but lately restored to varietal prominence in the Vin de Pays des Côtes de Gascogne where high-tech wineries turn it into a fresh and crisp, if unchallenging, dry wine at a budget price. But beware, cheap Colombard (especially from South Africa) can still be very dull.

Conca de Barbera – Winemaking region of Catalonia, Spain.

co-op – Very many of France's good-quality, inexpensive wines are made by co-operatives. These are wine-producing factories whose members, and joint-owners, are local *vignerons* (vine growers). Each year they sell their harvests to the co-op for turning into branded wines. In Italy, co-op wines can be identified by the words *Cantina Sociale* on the label and in Germany by the term *Winzergenossenschaft*.

Corbières – A name to look out for. It's an AC of France's Midi (deep south) and produces countless robust reds and a few interesting whites, often at bargain prices.

Cortese – White grape variety of Piedmont, Italy. At its best, makes amazingly delicious, keenly brisk and fascinating wines, including those of the Gavi DOCG. Worth seeking out.

Costières de Nîmes – Until 1989, this AC of southern France was known as the Costières de Gard. It forms a buffer between the southern Rhône and Languedoc-Roussillon regions, and makes wines from broadly the same range of grape varieties. It's a name to look out for, the best red wines being notable for their concentration of colour and fruit, with the earthy-spiciness of the better Rhône wines and a likeable liquorice note. A few good white wines, too, and even a decent rosé or two.

Côte – In French, it simply means a side, or slope, of a hill. The implication in wine terms is that the grapes come from a vineyard ideally situated for maximum sunlight, good drainage and the unique soil conditions prevailing on the hill in question. It's fair enough to claim that vines grown on slopes might get more sunlight than those grown on the flat, but there is no guarantee whatsoever that any wine labelled 'Côtes du' this or that is made from grapes grown on a hillside anyway. Côtes du Rhône wines are a case in point. Many 'Côtes' wines come from entirely level vineyards and it is worth remembering that many of the vineyards of Bordeaux, producing most of the world's priciest wines, are little short of prairie-flat. The quality factor is determined much more significantly by the weather and the talents of the winemaker.

Coteaux Bourguignons – Generic AC of Burgundy, France, since 2011 for red and rosé wines from Pinot Noir and Gamay grapes, and white wines from (principally) Chardonnay and Bourgogne Aligoté grapes. The AC replaces the former appellation Bourgogne Grand Ordinaire.

Côtes de Blaye – Appellation Contrôlée zone of Bordeaux on the right bank of the River Gironde, opposite the more prestigious Médoc zone of the left bank. Best-rated vineyards qualify for the AC Premières Côtes de Blaye. A couple of centuries ago, Blaye (pronounced 'bligh') was the grander of the two, and even today makes some wines that compete well for quality, and at a fraction of the price of wines from its more fashionable rival across the water.

Côtes de Bourg – AC neighbouring Côtes de Blaye, making red wines of fast-improving quality and value.

Côtes du Luberon – Appellation Contrôlée zone of Provence in south-east France. Wines, mostly red, are similar in style to Côtes du Rhône.

Côtes du Rhône – One of the biggest and best-known appellations of south-east France, covering an area roughly defined by the southern reaches of the valley of the River Rhône. Long notorious for cheap and execrable reds, the Côtes du Rhône AC has lately achieved remarkable improvements in quality at all points along the price scale. Lots of brilliant-value warm and spicy reds, principally from Grenache and Syrah grapes. There are also some white and rosé wines.

Côtes du Rhône Villages – Appellation within the larger Côtes du Rhône AC for wine of supposed superiority made in a number of zones associated with a long list of nominated individual villages.

Côtes du Roussillon – Huge appellation of south-west France known for strong, dark, peppery reds often offering very decent value.

Côtes du Roussillon Villages – Appellation for superior wines from a number of nominated locations within the larger Roussillon AC. Some of these village wines can be of exceptional quality and value.

crianza – Means 'nursery' in Spanish. On Rioja and Navarra wines, the designation signifies a wine that has been nursed through a maturing period of at least a year in oak casks and a further six months in bottle before being released for sale.

cru – A word that crops up with confusing regularity on French wine labels. It means 'the growing' or 'the making' of a wine and asserts that the wine concerned is from a specific vineyard. Under the Appellation Contrôlée rules, countless *crus* are classified in various hierarchical ranks. Hundreds of individual vineyards are described as *premier cru* or *grand cru* in the classic wine regions of Alsace, Bordeaux, Burgundy and Champagne. The common denominator is that the wine can be counted on to be enormously expensive. On humbler wines, the use of the word *cru* tends to be mere decoration.

cru classé – *See* classed growth.

cuve – A vat for wine. French.

cuvée – French for the wine in a *cuve*, or vat. The word is much used on labels to imply that the wine is from just one vat, and thus of unique, unblended character. *Première cuvée* is supposedly the best wine from a given pressing because the grapes have had only the initial, gentle squashing to extract the free-run juice. Subsequent *cuvées* will have been from harsher pressings, grinding the grape pulp to extract the last drop of juice.

D

Dão – Major wine-producing region of northern Portugal now turning out much more interesting reds than it used to – worth looking out for anything made by mega-producer Sogrape.

demi sec – 'Half-dry' style of French (and some other) wines. Beware. It can mean anything from off-dry to cloyingly sweet.

DO – Denominación de Origen, Spain's wine-regulating scheme, similar to France's AC, but older – the first DO region was Rioja, from 1926. DO wines are Spain's best, accounting for a third of the nation's annual production.

DOC – Stands for Denominazione di Origine Controllata, Italy's equivalent of France's AC. The wines are made according to the stipulations of each of the system's 300-plus denominated zones of origin, along with a further 70-odd zones, which enjoy the superior classification of DOCG (DOC with *e Garantita* – guaranteed – appended).

Durif – Rare black grape variety mostly of California, where it is also known as Petite Sirah, but with some plantings in Australia.

E

earthy – A tricky word in the wine vocabulary. In this book, its use is meant to be complimentary. It indicates that the wine somehow suggests the soil the grapes were grown in, even (perhaps a shade too poetically) the landscape in which the vineyards lie. The amazing-value red wines of the torrid, volcanic southernmost regions of Italy are often described as earthy. This is an association with the pleasantly 'scorched' back-flavour in wines made from the ultra-ripe harvests of this near-sub-tropical part of the world.

edge – A wine with edge is one with evident (although not excessive) acidity.

élevé – 'Brought up' in French. Much used on wine labels where the wine has been matured (brought up) in oak barrels, *élevé en fûts de chêne*, to give it extra dimensions.

Entre Deux Mers – Meaning 'between two seas', it's a region lying between the Dordogne and Garonne rivers of Bordeaux, now mainly known for dry white wines from Sauvignon and Semillon grapes.

Estremadura – Wine-producing region occupying Portugal's coastal area north of Lisbon. Lots of interesting wines from indigenous grape varieties, usually at bargain prices. If a label mentions Estremadura, it is a safe rule that there might be something good within.

Extremadura – Minor wine-producing region of western Spain abutting the frontier with Portugal's Alentejo region. Not to be confused with Estremadura of Portugal (above).

F

Falanghina – Revived ancient grape variety of southern Italy now making some superbly fresh and tangy white wines.

Faugères – AC of the Languedoc in south-west France. Source of many hearty, economic reds.

Feteasca – White grape variety widely grown in Romania. Name means 'maiden's grape' and the wine tends to be soft and slightly sweet.

Fiano – White grape variety of the Campania of southern Italy and Sicily, lately revived. It is said to have been cultivated by the ancient Romans for a wine called Apianum.

finish – The last flavour lingering in the mouth after wine has been swallowed.

fino – Pale and very dry style of sherry. You drink it thoroughly chilled – and you don't keep it any longer after opening than other dry white wines. Needs to be fresh to be at its best.

Fitou – One of the first 'designer' wines, it's an appellation in France's Languedoc region, where production is dominated by one huge co-operative, the Vignerons de Mont Tauch. Back in the 1970s, this co-op paid a corporate-image company to come up with a Fitou logo and label-design style, and the wines have prospered ever since. And it's not just packaging – Fitou at all price levels can be very good value, especially from the Mont Tauch co-op.

flabby – Fun word describing a wine that tastes dilute or watery, with insufficient acidity.

Frappato – Black grape variety of Sicily. Light red wines.

fruit – In tasting terms, the fruit is the greater part of the overall flavour of a wine. The wine is (or should be) after all, composed entirely of fruit.

G

Gamay – The black grape that makes all red Beaujolais and some ordinary burgundy. It is a pretty safe rule to avoid Gamay wines from any other region, but there are exceptions.

Garganega – White grape variety of the Veneto region of north-east Italy. Best known as the principal ingredient of Soave, but occasionally included in varietal blends and mentioned as such on labels. Correctly pronounced 'gar-GAN-iga'.

Garnacha – Spanish black grape variety synonymous with Grenache of France. It is blended with Tempranillo to make the red wines of Rioja and Navarra, and is now quite widely cultivated elsewhere in Spain to make grippingly fruity varietals.

garrigue – Arid land of France's deep south giving its name to a style of red wine that notionally evokes the herby, heated, peppery flavours associated with such a landscape. A tricky metaphor!

Gavi – DOCG for dry but rich white wine from Cortese grapes in Piedmont, north-west Italy. Trendy Gavi di Gavi wines tend to be enjoyably lush, but are rather expensive.

Gewürztraminer – One of the great grape varieties of Alsace, France. At their best, the wines are perfumed with lychees and are richly, spicily fruity, yet quite dry. Gewürztraminer from Alsace is almost always relatively expensive, but the grape is also grown with some success in Eastern Europe, Germany, Italy, New Zealand and South America, and sold at more approachable prices. Pronounced 'ge-VOORTS-traminer'.

Givry – AC for red and white wines in the Côte Chalonnaise sub-region of Burgundy. Source of some wonderfully natural-tasting reds that might be lighter than those of the more prestigious Côte d'Or to the north, but have great merits of their own. Relatively, the wines are often underpriced.

Glera – Alternative name for Prosecco grape of northern Italy.

Graciano – Black grape variety of Spain that is one of the minor constituents of Rioja. Better known in its own right in Australia where it can make dense, spicy, long-lived red wines.

green – I don't often use this in the pejorative. Green, to me, is a likeable degree of freshness, especially in Sauvignon Blanc wines.

Grecanico – White grape variety of southern Italy, especially Sicily. Aromatic, grassy dry white wines.

Greco – White grape variety of southern Italy believed to be of ancient Greek origin. Big-flavoured dry white wines.

Grenache – The mainstay of the wines of the southern Rhône Valley in France. Grenache is usually the greater part of the mix in Côtes du Rhône reds and is widely planted right across the neighbouring Languedoc-Roussillon region. It's a big-cropping variety that thrives even in the hottest climates and is really a blending grape – most commonly with Syrah, the noble variety of the northern Rhône. Few French wines are labelled with its name, but the grape has caught on in Australia in a big way and it is now becoming a familiar varietal, known for strong, dark liquorous reds. Grenache is the French name for what is originally a Spanish variety, Garnacha.

Grillo – White grape of Sicily said to be among the island's oldest indigenous varieties, pre-dating the arrival of the Greeks in 600 BC. Much used for fortified Marsala, it has lately been revived for interesting, aromatic dry table wines.

grip – In wine-tasting terminology, the sensation in the mouth produced by a wine that has a healthy quantity of tannin in it. A wine with grip is a good wine. A wine with too much tannin, or which is still too young (the tannin hasn't 'softened' with age) is not described as having grip, but as mouth-puckering – or simply undrinkable.

Grolleau – Black grape variety of the Loire Valley principally cultivated for Rosé d'Anjou.

Gros Plant – White grape variety of the Pays Nantais in France's Loire estuary; synonymous with the Folle Blanche grape of south-west France.

Grüner Veltliner – The 'national' white-wine grape of Austria. In the past it made mostly soft, German-style everyday wines, but now is behind some excellent dry styles, too.

H

halbtrocken – 'Half-dry' in Germany's wine vocabulary. A reassurance that the wine is not some ghastly sugared Liebfraumilch-style confection.

hard – In red wine, a flavour denoting excess tannin, probably due to immaturity.

Haut-Médoc – Extensive AOC of Bordeaux accounting for the greater part of the vineyard area to the north of the city of Bordeaux and west of the Gironde river. The Haut-Médoc incorporates the prestigious commune-AOCs of Listrac, Margaux, Moulis, Pauillac, St Estephe and St Julien.

hock – The wine of Germany's Rhine river valleys. Traditionally, but no longer consistently, it comes in brown bottles, as distinct from the wine of the Mosel river valleys – which comes in green ones.

I

Indication Géographique Protégée (IGP) – Introduced to France in 2010 under new EU-wide wine-designation rules, IGP covers the wines hitherto known as vins de pays. Some wines are already being labelled IGP, but established vins de pays producers are unlikely to redesignate their products in a hurry, and are not obliged to do so. Some will abbreviate, so, for example, Vin de Pays d'Oc shortens to Pays d'Oc.

Indicazione Geografica Tipica – Italian wine-quality designation, broadly equivalent to France's vin de pays. The label has to state the geographical location of the vineyard and will often (but not always) state the principal grape varieties from which the wine is made.

isinglass – A gelatinous material used in fining (clarifying) wine. It is derived from fish bladders and consequently is eschewed by makers of 'vegetarian' wines.

J

jammy – The 'sweetness' in dry red wines is supposed to evoke ripeness rather than sugariness. Sometimes, flavours include a sweetness reminiscent of jam. Usually a fault in the winemaking technique.

Jerez – Wine town of Andalucia, Spain, and home to sherry. The English word 'sherry' is a simple mispronunciation of Jerez.

joven – Young wine, Spanish. In regions such as Rioja, *vino joven* is a synonym for *sin crianza*, which means 'without ageing' in cask or bottle.

Jura – Wine region of eastern France incorporating four AOCs, Arbois, Château-Chalon, Côtes du Jura and L'Etoile. Known for still red, white and rosé wines and sparkling wines as well as exotic *vin de paille* and *vin jaune*.

Juraçon – Appellation for white wines from Courbu and Manseng grapes at Pau, south-west France.

K

Kabinett – Under Germany's bewildering wine-quality rules, this is a classification of a top-quality (QmP) wine. Expect a keen, dry, racy style. The name comes from the cabinet or cupboard in which winemakers traditionally kept their most treasured bottles.

Kekfrankos – Black grape variety of Hungary, particularly the Sopron region, which makes some of the country's more interesting red wines, characterised by colour and spiciness. Same variety as Austria's Blaufrankisch.

L

Ladoix – Unfashionable AC at northern edge of Côtes de Beaune makes some of

Burgundy's true bargain reds. A name to look out for.

Lambrusco – The name is that of a black grape variety widely grown across northern Italy. True Lambrusco wine is red, dry and very slightly sparkling, but from the 1980s Britain has been deluged with a strange, sweet manifestation of the style, which has done little to enhance the good name of the original. Good Lambrusco is delicious and fun, but in this country now very hard to find.

Languedoc-Roussillon – Vast area of southern France, including the country's south-west Mediterranean region. The source, now, of many great-value wines from countless ACs and vin de pays zones.

lees – The detritus of the winemaking process that collects in the bottom of the vat or cask. Wines left for extended periods on the lees can acquire extra dimensions of flavour, in particular a 'leesy' creaminess.

legs – The liquid residue left clinging to the sides of the glass after wine has been swirled. The persistence of the legs is an indicator of the weight of alcohol. Also known as 'tears'.

lieu dit – This is starting to appear on French wine labels. It translates as an 'agreed place' and is an area of vineyard defined as of particular character or merit, but not classified under wine law. Usually, the *lieu dit*'s name is stated, with the implication that the wine in question has special value.

liquorice – The pungent slightly burnt flavours of this once-fashionable confection are detectable in some wines made from very ripe grapes, for example, the Malbec harvested in Argentina and several varieties grown in the very hot vineyards of southernmost Italy. A close synonym is 'tarry'. This characteristic is by no means a fault in red wine, unless very dominant, but it can make for a challenging flavour that might not appeal to all tastes.

liquorous – Wines of great weight and glyceriney texture (evidenced by the 'legs', or 'tears', which cling to the glass after the wine has been swirled) are always noteworthy. The connection with liquor is drawn in respect of the feel of the wine in the mouth, rather than with the higher alcoholic strength of spirits.

Lirac – Village and AOC of southern Rhône Valley, France. A near-neighbour of the esteemed appellation of Châteauneuf du Pape, Lirac makes red wine of comparable depth and complexity, at competitive prices.

Lugana – DOC of Lombardy, Italy, known for a dry white wine that is often of real distinction – rich, almondy stuff from the ubiquitous Trebbiano grape.

M

Macabeo – One of the main grapes used for cava, the sparkling wine of Spain. It is the same grape as Viura.

Mâcon – Town and collective appellation of southern Burgundy, France. Lightweight white wines from Chardonnay grapes and similarly light reds from Pinot Noir and some Gamay. The better ones, and the ones exported, have the AC Mâcon-Villages and there are individual village wines with their own ACs including Mâcon-Clessé, Mâcon-Viré and Mâcon-Lugny.

Malbec – Black grape variety grown on a small scale in Bordeaux, and the mainstay of the wines of Cahors in France's Dordogne region under the name Cot. Now much better known for producing big butch reds in Argentina.

manzanilla – Pale, very dry sherry of Sanlucar de Barrameda, a resort town on the Bay of Cadiz in Spain. Manzanilla is proud to be distinct from the pale, very dry fino sherry of the main producing town of Jerez de la Frontera an hour's drive inland. Drink it chilled and fresh – it goes downhill in an opened bottle after just a few days, even if kept (as it should be) in the fridge.

Margaret River – Vineyard region of Western Australia regarded as ideal for grape varieties including Cabernet Sauvignon. It has a relatively cool climate and a reputation for making sophisticated wines, both red and white.

Marlborough – Best-known vineyard region of New Zealand's South Island has a cool climate and a name for brisk but cerebral Sauvignon Blanc and Chardonnay wines.

Marsanne – White grape variety of the northern Rhône Valley and, increasingly, of the wider south of France. It's known for making well-coloured wines with heady aroma and fruit.

Mataro – Black grape variety of Australia. It's the same as the Mourvèdre of France and Monastrell of Spain.

Mazuelo – Spanish name for France's black grape variety Carignan.

McLaren Vale – Vineyard region south of Adelaide in south-east Australia. Known for blockbuster Shiraz (and Chardonnay) that can be of great balance and quality from winemakers who keep the ripeness under control.

meaty – Weighty, rich red wine style.

Mencia – Black grape variety of Galicia and north-west Spain. Light red wines.

Mendoza – The region to watch in Argentina. Lying to the east of the Andes mountains, just about opposite the best vineyards of Chile on the other side, Mendoza accounts for the bulk of Argentine wine production, with quality improving fast.

Merlot – One of the great black wine grapes of Bordeaux, and now grown all over the world. The name is said to derive from the French *merle*, meaning a blackbird. Characteristics of Merlot-based wines attract descriptions such as 'plummy' and 'plump' with black-cherry aroma. The grapes are larger than most, and thus have less skin in proportion to their flesh. This means the resulting wines have less tannin than wines from smaller-berry varieties such as Cabernet Sauvignon, and are therefore, in the Bordeaux context at least, more suitable for drinking while still relatively young.

middle palate – In wine tasting, the impression given by the wine when it is held in the mouth.

Midi – Catch-all term for the deep south of France west of the Rhône Valley.

mineral – I am trying to excise this overused word from my notes, but not so far managing to do so with much conviction. To me it evokes flavours such as the stone-pure freshness of some Loire dry whites, or the steely quality of the more austere style of the Chardonnay grape, especially in Chablis. Mineral really just means something mined, as in dug out of the ground, like iron ore (as in steel) or rock, as in, er, stone. Maybe there's something in it, but I am not entirely confident.

Minervois – AC for (mostly) red wines from vineyards around the town of Minerve in the Languedoc-Roussillon region of France. Often good value. The new Minervois La Livinière AC – a sort of Minervois *grand cru* – is host to some great estates including Château Maris and Vignobles Lorgeril.

Monastrell – Black grape variety of Spain, widely planted in Mediterranean regions for inexpensive wines notable for their high alcohol and toughness – though they can mature into excellent, soft reds. The variety is known in France as Mourvèdre and in Australia as Mataro.

Monbazillac – AC for sweet, dessert wines within the wider appellation of Bergerac in south-west France. Made from the same grape varieties (principally Sauvignon and Semillon) that go into the much costlier counterpart wines of Barsac and Sauternes near Bordeaux, these stickies from botrytis-affected, late-harvested grapes can be delicious and good value for money.

Montalcino – Hill town of Tuscany, Italy, and a DOCG for strong and very long-lived red wines from Brunello grapes. The wines are mostly very expensive. Rosso di Montalcino, a DOC for the humbler wines of the zone, is often a good buy.

Montepulciano – Black grape variety of Italy. Best known in Montepulciano d'Abruzzo, the juicy, purply-black and bramble-fruited red of the Abruzzi region midway down Italy's Adriatic side. Also the grape in the rightly popular hearty reds of Rosso Conero from around Ancona in the Marches. Not to be confused with the hill town of Montepulciano in Tuscany, famous for expensive Vino Nobile di Montepulciano wine.

morello – Lots of red wines have smells and flavours redolent of cherries. Morello cherries, among the darkest coloured and sweetest of all varieties and the preferred choice of cherry-brandy producers, have a distinct sweetness resembled by some wines made from Merlot grapes. A morello whiff or taste is generally very welcome.

Moscatel – Spanish Muscat.

Moscato – *See* Muscat.

Moselle – The wine of Germany's Mosel river valleys, collectively known for winemaking purposes as Mosel-Saar-Ruwer. The wine always comes in slim, green bottles, as distinct from the brown bottles traditionally, but no longer exclusively, employed for Rhine wines.

Mourvèdre – Widely planted black grape variety of southern France. It's an ingredient in many of the wines of Provence, the Rhône and Languedoc, including the ubiquitous Vin de Pays d'Oc. It's a hot-climate vine and the wine is usually blended with other varieties to give sweet aromas and 'backbone' to the mix. Known as Mataro in Australia and Monastrell in Spain.

Muscadet – One of France's most familiar everyday whites, made from a grape called the Melon or Melon de Bourgogne. It comes from vineyards at the estuarial end of the River Loire, and has a sea-breezy freshness about it. The better wines are reckoned to be those from the vineyards in the Sèvre et Maine region, and many are made *sur lie* – 'on the lees' – meaning that the wine is left in contact with the yeasty deposit of its fermentation until just before bottling, in an endeavour to add interest to what can sometimes be an acidic and fruitless style.

Muscat – Grape variety with origins in ancient Greece, and still grown widely among the Aegean islands for the production of sweet white wines. Muscats are the wines that taste more like grape juice than any other – but the high sugar levels ensure they are also among the most alcoholic of wines, too. Known as Moscato in Italy, the grape is much used for making sweet sparkling wines, as in Asti Spumante or Moscato d'Asti. There are several appellations in south-west France for inexpensive Muscats made rather like port, part-fermented before the addition of grape alcohol to halt the conversion of sugar into alcohol, creating a sweet and heady *vin doux naturel*. Dry Muscat wines, when well made, have a delicious sweet aroma but a refreshing, light touch with flavours reminiscent variously of orange blossom, wood smoke and grapefruit.

must – New-pressed grape juice prior to fermentation.

N

Navarra – DO wine-producing region of northern Spain adjacent to, and overshadowed by, Rioja. Navarra's wines can be startlingly akin to their neighbouring rivals, and sometimes rather better value for money.

négociant – In France, a dealer-producer who buys wines from growers and matures and/or blends them for sale under his or her own label. Purists can be a bit sniffy about these entrepreneurs, claiming that only the vine-grower with his or her own winemaking set-up can make truly authentic stuff, but the truth is that many of the best wines of France are *négociant*-produced – especially at the humbler end of the price scale. *Négociants* are often identified on wine labels as *négociant-éleveur* (literally 'dealer-bringer-up'), meaning that the wine has been matured, blended and bottled by the party in question.

Negroamaro – Black grape variety mainly of Apulia, the much-lauded wine region of south-east Italy. Dense, earthy red wines with ageing potential and plenty of alcohol. The grape behind Copertino.

Nerello Mascalese – Black grape of Sicily making light, flavoursome and alcoholic reds.

Nero d'Avola – Black grape variety of Sicily and southern Italy. It makes deep-coloured wines that, given half a chance, can develop intensity and richness with age.

non-vintage – A wine is described as such when it has been blended from the harvests of more than one year. A non-vintage wine is not necessarily an inferior one, but under quality-control regulations around the world, still table wines most usually derive solely from one year's grape crop to qualify for appellation status. Champagnes and sparkling wines are mostly blended from several vintages, as are fortified wines, such as basic port and sherry.

nose – In the vocabulary of the wine-taster, the nose is the scent of a wine. Sounds a bit dotty, but it makes a sensible enough alternative to the rather bald 'smell'. The use of the word 'perfume' implies that the wine smells particularly good. 'Aroma' is used specifically to describe a wine that smells as it should, as in 'this burgundy has the authentic strawberry-raspberry aroma of Pinot Noir'.

O

oak – Most of the world's costliest wines are matured in new or nearly new oak barrels, giving additional opulence of flavour. Of late, many cheaper wines have been getting the oak treatment, too, in older, cheaper casks, or simply by having sacks of oak chippings poured into their steel or fibreglass holding tanks. 'Oak aged' on a label is likely to indicate the latter treatments. But the overtly oaked wines of Australia have in some cases been so overdone that there is now a reactive trend whereby some producers proclaim their wines – particularly Chardonnays – as 'unoaked' on the label, thereby asserting that the flavours are more naturally achieved.

Oltrepo Pavese – Wine-producing zone of Piedmont, north-west Italy. The name means 'south of Pavia across the [river] Po' and the wines, both white and red, can be excellent quality and value for money.

organic wine – As in other sectors of the food industry, demand for organically made wine is – or appears to be – growing. As a rule, a wine qualifies as organic if it comes entirely from grapes grown in vineyards cultivated without the use of synthetic materials, and made in a winery where chemical treatments or additives are shunned with similar vigour. In fact, there are plenty of winemakers in the world using organic methods, but who disdain to label their bottles as such. Wines proclaiming their organic status used to carry the same sort of premium as their counterparts round the corner in the fruit, vegetable and meat aisles. But organic viticulture is now commonplace and there seems little price impact. There is no single worldwide (or even Europe-wide) standard for organic food or wine, so you pretty much have to take the producer's word for it.

P

Pasqua – One of the biggest and, it should be said, best wine producers of the Veneto region of north-west Italy.

Passetoutgrains – Bourgogne Passetoutgrains is a generic appellation of the Burgundy region, France. The word loosely means 'any grapes allowed' and is supposed specifically to designate a red wine made with Gamay grapes as well as Burgundy's principal black variety, Pinot Noir, in a ratio of two parts Gamay to one of Pinot. The wine is usually relatively inexpensive, and relatively uninteresting, too.

Pays d'Oc – Shortened form under recent rule changes of French wine designation Vin de Pays d'Oc. All other similar regional designations can be similarly abbreviated.

Pecorino – White grape variety of mid-eastern Italy currently in vogue for well-coloured dry white white varietal wines.

Periquita – Black grape variety of southern Portugal. Makes rather exotic spicy reds. Name means 'parrot'.

Perricone – Black grape variety of Sicily. Low-acid red wines.

PET – It's what they call plastic wine bottles – lighter to transport and allegedly as ecological as glass. Polyethylene terephthalate.

Petit Verdot – Black grape variety of Bordeaux used to give additional colour, density and spiciness to Cabernet Sauvignon-dominated blends. Mostly a minority player at home, but in Australia and California it is grown as the principal variety for some big hearty reds of real character.

petrol – When white wines from certain grapes, especially Riesling, are allowed to age in the bottle for longer than a year or two, they can take on a spirity aroma reminiscent of petrol or diesel. In grand mature German wines, this is considered a very good thing.

Picpoul – Grape variety of southern France. Best known in Picpoul de Pinet, a dry white from near Carcassonne in the Languedoc, newly elevated to AOP status. The name Picpoul means 'stings the lips' – referring to the natural high acidity of the juice.

Piemonte – North-western province of Italy, which we call Piedmont, known for the spumante wines of the town of Asti, plus expensive Barbaresco and Barolo and better-value varietal red wines from Barbera and Dolcetto grapes.

Pinotage – South Africa's own black grape variety. Makes red wines ranging from light and juicy to dark, strong and long-lived. It's a cross between Pinot Noir and a grape the South Africans used to call Hermitage (thus the portmanteau name) but turns out to have been Cinsault.

Pinot Blanc – White grape variety principally of Alsace, France. Florally perfumed, exotically fruity dry white wines.

Pinot Grigio – White grape variety of northern Italy. Wines bearing its name are perplexingly fashionable. Good examples have an interesting smoky-pungent aroma and keen, slaking fruit. But most are dull. Originally French, it is at its best in the lushly exotic Pinot Gris wines of Alsace and is also successfully cultivated in Germany and New Zealand.

Pinot Noir – The great black grape of Burgundy, France. It makes all the region's fabulously expensive red wines. Notoriously difficult to grow in warmer climates, it is nevertheless cultivated by countless intrepid winemakers in the New World intent on reproducing the magic appeal of red burgundy. California and New Zealand have come closest, but rarely at prices much below those for the real thing. Some Chilean Pinot Noirs are inexpensive and worth trying.

Pouilly Fuissé – Village and AC of the Mâconnais region of southern Burgundy in France. Dry white wines from Chardonnay grapes. Wines are among the highest rated of the Mâconnais.

Pouilly Fumé – Village and AC of the Loire Valley in France. Dry white wines from Sauvignon Blanc grapes. Similar 'pebbly', 'grassy' or even 'gooseberry' style to neighbouring AC Sancerre. The notion put about by some enthusiasts that Pouilly Fumé is 'smoky' is surely nothing more than word association with the name.

Primitivo – Black grape variety of southern Italy, especially the region of Puglia. Named from Latin *primus* for first, the grape is among the earliest-ripening of all varieties. The wines are typically dense and dark in colour with plenty of alcohol, and have an earthy, spicy style. Often a real bargain.

Prosecco – White grape variety of Italy's Veneto region known entirely for the softly sparkling wine it makes. The best come from the DOC Conegliano-Valdobbiadene, made as spumante ('foaming') wines in pressurised tanks, typically to 11 per cent alcohol and ranging from softly sweet to crisply dry. Now trendy, but the cheap wines – one leading brand comes in a can – are of very variable quality.

Puglia – The region occupying the 'heel' of southern Italy, lately making many good, inexpensive wines from indigenous grape varieties.

Q

QbA – German, standing for Qualitätswein bestimmter Anbaugebiete. It means 'quality wine from designated areas' and implies that the wine is made from grapes with a minimum level of ripeness, but it's by no means a guarantee of exciting quality. Only wines labelled QmP (see next entry) can be depended upon to be special.

QmP – Stands for Qualitätswein mit Prädikat. These are the serious wines of Germany, made without the addition of sugar to 'improve' them. To qualify for QmP status, the grapes must reach a level of ripeness as measured on a sweetness scale – all according to Germany's fiendishly complicated wine-quality regulations. Wines from grapes that reach the stated minimum level of sweetness qualify for the description of Kabinett. The next level up earns the rank of Spätlese, meaning 'late-picked'. Kabinett wines can be expected to be dry and brisk in style, and Spätlese wines a little bit riper and fuller. The next grade up, Auslese, meaning 'selected harvest', indicates a wine made from super-ripe grapes; it will be golden in colour and honeyed in flavour. A generation ago, these wines were as valued, and as expensive, as any of the world's grandest appellations, but the collapse in demand for German wines in the UK – brought about by the disrepute rightly earned for floods of filthy Liebfraumilch – means they are now seriously undervalued.

Quincy – AC of Loire Valley, France, known for pebbly-dry white wines from Sauvignon grapes. The wines are forever compared to those of nearby and much better-known Sancerre – and Quincy often represents better value for money. Pronounced 'KAN-see'.

Quinta – Portuguese for farm or estate. It precedes the names of many of Portugal's best-known wines. It is pronounced 'KEEN-ta'.

R

racy – Evocative wine-tasting description for wine that thrills the tastebuds with a rush of exciting sensations. Good Rieslings often qualify.

raisiny – Wines from grapes that have been very ripe or overripe at harvest can take on a smell and flavour akin to the concentrated, heat-dried sweetness of raisins. As a minor element in the character of a wine, this can add to the appeal but as a dominant characteristic it is a fault.

rancio – Spanish term harking back to Roman times when wines were commonly stored in jars outside, exposed to the sun, so they oxidised and took on a burnt sort of flavour. Today, *rancio* describes a baked – and by no means unpleasant – flavour in fortified wines, particularly sherry and Madeira.

Reserva – In Portugal and Spain, this has genuine significance. The Portuguese use it for special wines with a higher alcohol level and longer ageing, although the precise periods vary between regions. In Spain, especially in the Navarra and Rioja regions, it means the wine must have had at least a year in oak and two in bottle before release.

reserve – On French (as *réserve*) or other wines, this implies special-quality, longer-aged wines, but has no official significance.

Retsina – The universal white wine of Greece. It has been traditionally made in Attica, the region of Athens, for a very long time, and is said to owe its origins and name to the ancient custom of sealing amphorae (terracotta jars) of the wine with a gum made from pine resin. Some of the flavour of the resin inevitably transmitted itself into the wine, and ancient Greeks acquired a lasting taste for it.

Reuilly – AC of Loire Valley, France, for crisp dry whites from Sauvignon grapes. Pronounced 'RER-yee'.

Ribatejo – Emerging wine region of Portugal. Worth seeking out on labels of red wines in particular, because new winemakers are producing lively stuff from distinctive indigenous grapes such as Castelao and Trincadeira.

Ribera del Duero – Classic wine region of north-west Spain lying along the River Duero (which crosses the border to become Portugal's Douro, forming the valley where port comes from). It is home to an estate rather oddly named Vega Sicilia, where red wines of epic quality are made and sold at equally epic prices. Further down the scale, some very good reds are made, too.

Riesling – The noble grape variety of Germany. It is correctly pronounced 'REEZ-ling', not 'RICE-ling'. Once notorious as the grape behind all those boring 'medium' Liebfraumilches and Niersteiners, this grape has had a bad press. In fact, there has never been much, if any, Riesling in Germany's cheap-and-nasty plonks. But the country's best wines, the so-called Qualitätswein mit Prädikat grades, are made almost exclusively with Riesling. These wines range from crisply fresh and appley styles to extravagantly fruity, honeyed wines from late-harvested grapes. Excellent Riesling wines are also made in Alsace and now in Australia.

Rioja – The principal fine-wine region of Spain, in the country's north east. The pricier wines are noted for their vanilla-pod richness from long ageing in oak casks. Tempranillo and Garnacha grapes make the reds, Viura the whites.

Ripasso – A particular style of Valpolicella wine. New wine is partially refermented in vats that have been used to make the Recioto reds (wines made from semi-dried grapes), thus creating a bigger, smoother version of usually light and pale Valpolicella.

Riserva – In Italy, a wine made only in the best vintages, and allowed longer ageing in cask and bottle.

Rivaner – Alternative name for Germany's Müller-Thurgau grape, the life-blood of Liebfraumilch.

Riverland – Vineyard region to the immediate north of the Barossa Valley of

South Australia, extending east into New South Wales.

Roditis – White grape variety of Greece, known for fresh dry whites with decent acidity, often included in retsina.

rosso – Red wine, Italy.

Rosso Conero – DOC red wine made in the environs of Ancona in the Marches, Italy. Made from the Montepulciano grape, the wine can provide excellent value for money.

Ruby Cabernet – Black grape variety of California, created by crossing Cabernet Sauvignon and Carignan. Makes soft and squelchy red wine at home and in South Africa.

Rueda – DO of north-west Spain making first-class refreshing dry whites from the indigenous Verdejo grape, imported Sauvignon, and others. Exciting quality, and prices are keen.

Rully – AC of Chalonnais region of southern Burgundy, France. White wines from Chardonnay and red wines from Pinot Noir grapes. Both can be very good and are substantially cheaper than their more northerly Burgundian neighbours. Pronounced 'ROO-yee'.

S

Saint Emilion – AC of Bordeaux, France. Centred on the romantic hill town of St Emilion, this famous sub-region makes some of the grandest red wines of France, but also some of the best-value ones. Less fashionable than the Médoc region on the opposite (west) bank of the River Gironde that bisects Bordeaux, St Emilion wines are made largely with the Merlot grape, and are relatively quick to mature. The grandest wines are classified *1er grand cru classé* and are madly expensive, but many more are classified respectively *grand cru classé* and *grand cru*, and these designations can be seen as a fairly trustworthy indicator of quality. There are several 'satellite' St Emilion ACs named after the villages at their centres, notably Lussac St Emilion, Montagne St Emilion and Puisseguin St Emilion. Some excellent wines are made by estates within these ACs, and at relatively affordable prices thanks to the comparatively humble status of their satellite designations.

Salento – Up-and-coming wine region of southern Italy. Many good bargain reds from local grapes including Nero d'Avola and Primitivo.

Sancerre – AC of the Loire Valley, France, renowned for flinty-fresh Sauvignon whites and rarer Pinot Noir reds. These wines are never cheap, and recent tastings make it plain that only the best-made, individual-producer wines are worth the money. Budget brands seem mostly dull.

Sangiovese – The local black grape of Tuscany, Italy. It is the principal variety used for Chianti and is now widely planted in Latin America – often making delicious, Chianti-like wines with characteristic cherryish-but-deeply-ripe fruit and a dry, clean finish. Chianti wines have become (unjustifiably) expensive in recent years and cheaper Italian wines such as those called Sangiovese di Toscana make a consoling substitute.

Saumur – Town and appellation of Loire Valley, France. Characterful minerally red wines from Cabernet Franc grapes, and some whites. The once-popular sparkling wines from Chenin Blanc grapes are now little seen in Britain.

Saumur-Champigny – Separate appellation for red wines from Cabernet Franc grapes of Saumur in the Loire, sometimes very good and lively.

Sauvignon Blanc – French white grape variety now grown worldwide. New Zealand is successfully challenging the long supremacy of French ACs such as

Sancerre. The wines are characterised by aromas of gooseberry, fresh-cut grass, even asparagus. Flavours are often described as 'grassy' or 'nettly'.

sec – Dry wine style. French.

secco – Dry wine style. Italian.

Semillon – White grape variety originally of Bordeaux, where it is blended with Sauvignon Blanc to make fresh dry whites and, when harvested very late in the season, the ambrosial sweet whites of Barsac, Sauternes and other appellations. Even in the driest wines, the grape can be recognised from its honeyed, sweet-pineapple, even banana-like aromas. Now widely planted in Australia and Latin America, and frequently blended with Chardonnay to make dry whites, some of them interesting.

sherry – The great aperitif wine of Spain, centred on the Andalusian city of Jerez (from which the name 'sherry' is an English mispronunciation). There is a lot of sherry-style wine in the world, but only the authentic wine from Jerez and the neighbouring producing towns of Puerta de Santa Maria and Sanlucar de Barrameda may label their wines as such. The Spanish drink real sherry – very dry and fresh, pale in colour and served well-chilled – called fino and manzanilla, and darker but naturally dry variations called amontillado, palo cortado and oloroso.

Shiraz – Australian name for the Syrah grape. The variety is the most widely planted of any in Australia, and makes red wines of wildly varying quality, characterised by dense colour, high alcohol, spicy fruit and generous, cushiony texture.

Somontano – Wine region of north-east Spain. Name means 'under the mountains' – in this case the Pyrenees – and the region has had DO status since 1984. Much innovative winemaking here, with New World styles emerging. Some very good buys. A region to watch.

souple – French wine-tasting term that translates into English as 'supple' or even 'docile' as in 'pliable', but I understand it in the vinous context to mean muscular but soft – a wine with tannin as well as soft fruit.

Spätlese – *See* QmP.

spirity – Some wines, mostly from the New World, are made from grapes so ripe at harvest that their high alcohol content can be detected through a mildly burning sensation on the tongue, similar to the effect of sipping a spirit.

spritzy – Describes a wine with a barely detectable sparkle. Some young wines are intended to have this elusive fizziness; in others it is a fault.

spumante – Sparkling wine of Italy. Asti Spumante is the best known, from the town of Asti in the north-west Italian province of Piemonte. The term describes wines that are fully sparkling. Frizzante wines have a less vigorous mousse.

stalky – A useful tasting term to describe red wines with flavours that make you think the stalks from the grape bunches must have been fermented along with the must (juice). Young Bordeaux reds very often have this mild astringency. In moderation it's fine, but if it dominates it probably signifies the wine is at best immature and at worst badly made.

Stellenbosch – Town and region at the heart of South Africa's burgeoning wine industry. It's an hour's drive from Cape Town and the source of much of the country's cheaper wine. Quality is variable, and the name Stellenbosch on a label can't (yet, anyway) be taken as a guarantee of quality.

stony – Wine-tasting term for keenly dry white wines. It's meant to indicate a wine of purity and real quality, with just the right match of fruit and acidity.

structured – Good wines are not one-dimensional, they have layers of flavour and texture. A structured wine has phases of enjoyment: the 'attack', or first impression in the mouth; the middle palate as the wine is held in the mouth; and the lingering aftertaste.

summer fruit – Wine-tasting term intended to convey a smell or taste of soft fruits such as strawberries and raspberries – without having to commit too specifically to which.

superiore – On labels of Italian wines, this is more than an idle boast. Under DOC rules, wines must qualify for the *superiore* designation by reaching one or more specified quality levels, usually a higher alcohol content or an additional period of maturation. Frascati, for example, qualifies for DOC status at 11.5 per cent alcohol, but to be classified *superiore* must have 12 per cent alcohol.

sur lie – Literally, 'on the lees'. It's a term now widely used on the labels of Muscadet wines, signifying that after fermentation has died down, the new wine has been left in the tank over the winter on the lees – the detritus of yeasts and other interesting compounds left over from the turbid fermentation process. The idea is that additional interest is imparted into the flavour of the wine.

Syrah – The noble grape of the Rhône Valley, France. Makes very dark, dense wine characterised by peppery, tarry aromas. Now planted all over southern France and farther afield. In Australia, where it makes wines ranging from disagreeably jam-like plonks to wonderfully rich and silky keeping wines, it is known as Shiraz.

T

table wine – Wine that is unfortified and of an alcoholic strength, for UK tax purposes anyway, of no more than 15 per cent. I use the term to distinguish, for example, between the red table wines of the Douro Valley in Portugal and the region's better-known fortified wine, port.

Tafelwein – Table wine, German. The humblest quality designation, which doesn't usually bode very well.

tank method – Bulk-production process for sparkling wines. Base wine undergoes secondary fermentation in a large, sealed vat rather than in individual closed bottles. Also known as the Charmat method after the name of the inventor of the process.

Tai – White grape variety of north-east Italy, a relative of Sauvignon Blanc. Also known in Italy as Tocai Friulano or, more correctly, Friulano.

Tannat – Black grape of south-west France, notably for wines of Madiran, and lately named as the variety most beneficial to health thanks to its outstanding antioxidant content.

tannin – Well known as the film-forming, teeth-coating component in tea, tannin is a natural compound that occurs in black grape skins and acts as a natural preservative in wine. Its noticeable presence in wine is regarded as a good thing. It gives young everyday reds their dryness, firmness of flavour and backbone. And it helps high-quality reds to retain their lively fruitiness for many years. A grand Bordeaux red when first made, for example, will have purply-sweet, rich fruit and mouth-puckering tannin, but after ten years or so this will have evolved into a delectably fruity, mature wine in which the formerly parching effects of the tannin have receded almost completely, leaving the shade of 'residual tannin' that marks out a great wine approaching maturity.

Tarrango – Black grape variety of Australia.

tarry – On the whole, winemakers don't like critics to say their wines evoke the redolence of road repairs, but I can't help using this term to describe the agreeable, sweet, 'burnt' flavour that is often found at the centre of the fruit in wines from Argentina, Italy and Portugal in particular.

TCA – Dreaded ailment in wine, usually blamed on faulty corks. It stands for 246 *trichloroanisol* and is characterised by a horrible musty smell and flavour in the affected wine. It is largely because of the current plague of TCA that so many wine producers worldwide are now going over to polymer 'corks' and screwcaps.

tears – The colourless alcohol in the wine left clinging to the inside of the glass after the contents have been swirled. Persistent tears (also known as 'legs') indicate a wine of good concentration.

Tempranillo – The great black grape of Spain. Along with Garnacha (Grenache in France) it makes all red Rioja and Navarra wines and, under many pseudonyms, is an important or exclusive contributor to the wines of many other regions of Spain. It is also widely cultivated in South America.

Teroldego – Black grape variety of Trentino, northern Italy. Often known as Teroldego Rotaliano after the Rotaliano region where most of the vineyards lie. Deep-coloured, assertive, green-edged red wines.

tinto – On Spanish labels indicates a deeply coloured red wine. Clarete denotes a paler colour. Also Portuguese.

Toro – Quality wine region east of Zamora, Spain.

Torrontes – White grape variety of Argentina. Makes soft, dry wines often with delicious grapey-spicy aroma, similar in style to the classic dry Muscat wines of Alsace, but at more accessible prices.

Touraine – Region encompassing a swathe of the Loire Valley, France. Non-AC wines may be labelled 'Sauvignon de Touraine' etc.

Touriga Nacional – The most valued black grape variety of the Douro Valley in Portugal, where port is made. The name Touriga now appears on an increasing number of table wines made as sidelines by the port producers. They can be very good, with the same spirity aroma and sleek flavours of port itself, minus the fortification.

Traminer – Grape variety, the same as Gewürztraminer.

Trebbiano – The workhorse white grape of Italy. A productive variety that is easy to cultivate, it seems to be included in just about every ordinary white wine of the entire nation – including Frascati, Orvieto and Soave. It is the same grape as France's Ugni Blanc. There are, however, distinct regional variations of the grape. Trebbiano di Lugana makes a distinctive white in the DOC of the name, sometimes very good, while Trebbiano di Toscana makes a major contribution to the distinctly less interesting dry whites of Chianti country.

Trincadeira Preta – Portuguese black grape variety native to the port-producing vineyards of the Douro Valley (where it goes under the name Tinta Amarella). In southern Portugal, it produces dark and sturdy table wines.

trocken – 'Dry' German wine. It's a recent trend among commercial-scale producers in the Rhine and Mosel to label their wines with this description in the hope of reassuring consumers that the contents do not resemble the dreaded sugar-water Liebfraumilch-type plonks of the bad old days. But the description does have a particular meaning under German wine law, namely that there is only a low level of unfermented sugar lingering in the wine (9 grams per litre, if you need to know), and this can leave the wine tasting rather austere.

U

Ugni Blanc – The most widely cultivated white grape variety of France and the mainstay of many a cheap dry white wine. To date it has been better known as the provider of base wine for distilling into armagnac and cognac, but lately the name has been appearing on wine labels. Technology seems to be improving the performance of the grape. The curious name is pronounced 'OON-yee', and is the same variety as Italy's ubiquitous Trebbiano.

Utiel-Requena – Region and *Denominación de Origen* of Mediterranean Spain inland from Valencia. Principally red wines from Bobal, Garnacha and Tempranillo grapes grown at relatively high altitude, between 600 and 900 metres.

V

Vacqueyras – Village of the southern Rhône Valley of France in the region better known for its generic appellation, the Côtes du Rhône. Vacqueyras can date its winemaking history all the way back to 1414, but has only been producing under its own village AC since 1991. The wines, from Grenache and Syrah grapes, can be wonderfully silky and intense, spicy and long-lived.

Valdepeñas – An island of quality production amidst the ocean of mediocrity that is Spain's La Mancha region – where most of the grapes are grown for distilling into the head-banging brandies of Jerez. Valdepeñas reds are made from a grape they call the Cencibel – which turns out to be a very close relation of the Tempranillo grape that is the mainstay of the fine but expensive red wines of Rioja. Again, like Rioja, Valdepeñas wines are matured in oak casks to give them a vanilla-rich smoothness. Among bargain reds, Valdepeñas is a name to look out for.

Valpolicella – Red wine of Verona, Italy. Good examples have ripe, cherry fruit and a pleasingly dry finish. Unfortunately, there are many bad examples of Valpolicella. Shop with circumspection. Valpolicella Classico wines, from the best vineyards clustered around the town, are more reliable. Those additionally labelled *superiore* have higher alcohol and some bottle age.

vanilla – Ageing wines in oak barrels (or, less picturesquely, adding oak chips to wine in huge concrete vats) imparts a range of characteristics including a smell of vanilla from the ethyl vanilline naturally given off by oak.

varietal – A varietal wine is one named after the grape variety (one or more) from which it is made. Nearly all everyday wines worldwide are now labelled in this way. It is salutary to contemplate that just 30 years ago, wines described thus were virtually unknown outside Germany and one or two quirky regions of France and Italy.

vegan-friendly – My informal way of noting that a wine is claimed to have been made not only with animal-product-free finings (*see* Vegetarian wine) but without any animal-related products whatsoever, such as manure in the vineyards.

vegetal – A tasting note definitely open to interpretation. It suggests a smell or flavour reminiscent less of fruit (apple, pineapple, strawberry and the like) than of something leafy or even root based. Some wines are evocative (to some tastes) of beetroot, cabbage or even unlikelier vegetable flavours – and these characteristics may add materially to the attraction of the wine.

vegetarian wine – Wines labelled 'suitable for vegetarians' have been made without the assistance of animal products for 'fining' – clarifying – before bottling. Gelatine, egg whites, isinglass from fish bladders and casein from milk are among the items shunned, usually in favour of bentonite, an absorbent clay first found at Benton in the US state of Montana.

Verdejo – White grape of the Rueda region in north-west Spain. It can make superbly perfumed crisp dry whites of truly distinctive character and has helped make Rueda one of the best white-wine sources of Europe. No relation to Verdelho.

Verdelho – Portuguese grape variety once mainly used for a medium-dry style of Madeira, also called Verdelho, but now rare. The vine is now prospering in Australia, where it can make well-balanced dry whites with fleeting richness and lemon-lime acidity.

Verdicchio – White grape variety of Italy best known in the DOC zone of Castelli di Jesi in the Adriatic wine region of the Marches. Dry white wines once known for little more than their naff amphora-style bottles but now gaining a reputation for interesting, herbaceous flavours of recognisable character.

Vermentino – White grape variety principally of Italy, especially Sardinia. Makes florally scented soft dry whites.

Vieilles vignes – Old vines. Many French producers like to claim on their labels that the wine within is from vines of notable antiquity. While it's true that vines don't produce useful grapes for the first few years after planting, it is uncertain whether vines of much greater age – say 25 years plus – than others actually make better fruit. There are no regulations governing the use of the term, so it's not a reliable indicator anyway.

Vin de France – In effect, the new Vin de Table of France's morphing wine laws. The term Vin de Table has just about disappeared – or should have, under new legislation introduced in 2010 – and Vin de France installed as the designation of a wine guaranteed to have been produced in France. The label may state the vintage (if all the wine in the blend does come from a single year's harvest) and the grape varieties that constitute the wine. It may not state the region of France from which the wine comes.

vin de liqueur – Sweet style of white wine mostly from the Pyrenean region of south-westernmost France, made by adding a little spirit to the new wine before it has fermented out, halting the fermentation and retaining sugar.

vin de pays – 'Country wine' of France. The French map is divided up into more than 100 vin de pays regions. Wine in bottles labelled as such must be from grapes grown in the nominated zone or *département*. Some vin de pays areas are huge: the Vin de Pays d'Oc (named after the Languedoc region) covers much of the Midi and Provence. Plenty of wines bearing this humble designation are of astoundingly high quality and certainly compete with New World counterparts for interest and value. *See* Indication Géographique Protégée.

vin de table – The humblest official classification of French wine. Neither the region, grape varieties nor vintage need be stated on the label. The wine might not even be French. Don't expect too much from this kind of 'table wine'. *See* Vin de France.

vin doux naturel – Sweet, mildly fortified wine of southern France. A little spirit is added during the winemaking process, halting the fermentation by killing the yeast before it has consumed all the sugars – hence the pronounced sweetness of the wine.

vin gris – Rosé wine from Provence.

Vinho de mesa – 'Table wine' of Portugal.

Vino da tavola – The humblest official classification of Italian wine. Much ordinary plonk bears this designation, but the bizarre quirks of Italy's wine laws dictate that some of that country's finest wines are also classed as mere vino da tavola (table wine). If an expensive Italian wine is labelled as such, it doesn't mean it will be a disappointment.

Vino de mesa – 'Table wine' of Spain. Usually very ordinary.

vintage – The grape harvest. The year displayed on bottle labels is the year of the harvest. Wines bearing no date have been blended from the harvests of two or more years.

Viognier – A grape variety once exclusive to the northern Rhône Valley in France where it makes a very chi-chi wine, Condrieu, usually costing £20 plus. Now, the Viognier is grown more widely, in North and South America as well as elsewhere in France, and occasionally produces soft, marrowy whites that echo the grand style of Condrieu itself. The Viognier is now commonly blended with Shiraz in red winemaking in Australia and South Africa. It does not dilute the colour and is confidently believed by highly experienced winemakers to enhance the quality. Steve Webber, in charge of winemaking at the revered De Bortoli estates in the Yarra Valley region of Victoria, Australia, puts between two and five per cent Viognier in with some of his Shiraz wines. 'I think it's the perfume,' he told me. 'It gives some femininity to the wine.'

Viura – White grape variety of Rioja, Spain. Also widely grown elsewhere in Spain under the name Macabeo. Wines have a blossomy aroma and are dry, but sometimes soft at the expense of acidity.

Vouvray – AC of the Loire Valley, France, known for still and sparkling dry white wines and sweet, still whites from late-harvested grapes. The wines, all from Chenin Blanc grapes, have a unique capacity for unctuous softness combined with lively freshness – an effect best portrayed in the demi-sec (slightly sweet) wines, which can be delicious and keenly priced. Unfashionable, but worth looking out for.

Vranac – Black grape variety of the Balkans known for dense colour and tangy-bitter edge to the flavour. Best enjoyed in situ.

W

weight – In an ideal world the weight of a wine is determined by the ripeness of the grapes from which it has been made. In some cases the weight is determined merely by the quantity of sugar added during the production process. A good, genuine wine described as having weight is one in which there is plenty of alcohol and 'extract' – colour and flavour from the grapes. Wine enthusiasts judge weight by swirling the wine in the glass and then examining the 'legs' or 'tears' left clinging to the inside of the glass after the contents have subsided. Alcohol gives these runlets a dense, glycerine-like condition, and if they cling for a long time, the wine is deemed to have weight – a very good thing in all honestly made wines.

Winzergenossenschaft – One of the many very lengthy and peculiar words regularly found on labels of German wines. This means a winemaking co-operative. Many excellent German wines are made by these associations of growers.

woodsap – A subjective tasting note. Some wines have a fleeting bitterness, which is not a fault, but an interesting balancing factor amidst very ripe flavours. The effect somehow evokes woodsap.

X

Xarel-lo – One of the main grape varieties for cava, the sparkling wine of Spain.

Xinomavro – Black grape variety of Greece. It retains its acidity even in the very hot conditions that prevail in many Greek vineyards, where harvests tend to over-ripen and make cooked-tasting wines. Modern winemaking techniques are capable of making well-balanced wines from Xinomavro.

Y

Yecla – Town and DO wine region of eastern Spain, close to Alicante, making lots of interesting, strong-flavoured red and white wines, often at bargain prices.

yellow – White wines are not white at all, but various shades of yellow – or, more poetically, gold. Some white wines with opulent richness even have a flavour I cannot resist calling yellow – reminiscent of butter.

Z

Zibibbo – Sicilian white grape variety synonymous with north African variety Muscat of Alexandria. Scantily employed in sweet winemaking, and occasionally for drier styles.

Zinfandel – Black grape variety of California. Makes brambly reds, some of which can age very gracefully, and 'blush' whites – actually pink, because a little of the skin colour is allowed to leach into the must. The vine is also planted in Australia and South America. The Primitivo of southern Italy is said to be a related variety, but makes a very different kind of wine.

Index